THE LIFE AND TIMES
OF TARQUIN
THE ETRUSCAN

By the same author

BEAU BRUMMELL: HIS LIFE AND TIMES

THE LIFE
AND TIMES
OF
TARQUIN
THE
ETRUSCAN

BY

CARLO MARIA FRANZERO

c. 1

THE JOHN DAY COMPANY

NEW YORK

934.

FRANZERO

First American edition 1961
© *Copyright, 1960, by Carlo Maria Franzero*

Map on page vi from **Grant Showerman**,
ROME AND THE ROMANS, Copyright 1931
by The Macmillan Company and used with
their permission.

Library of Congress Catalogue Card Number: 61-5692

CONTENTS

ILLUSTRATIONS

This much I will derive from my labor that, so long as I shall have my thoughts occupied in investigating the transactions of such distant ages, I shall withdraw myself from the sight of the many evils to which our eyes have been so long accustomed. —LIVY

PREFACE

It is a matter of surprise that Shakespeare did not develop his *Rape of Lucrece* into a full-length play, as the episode of Lucrece and the subsequent expulsion of the Etruscan kings from Rome has all the elements of a great tragedy. Indeed, the rape of Lucrece as a historical theme can be justifiably compared to the story of Helen of Troy. Had this small episode of lust and passion not occurred, perhaps Rome would never have risen to be the mother of the Latin civilization and mistress of the ancient world.

This dramatic theme of Shakespeare's poem stimulates the imagination and brings to mind a number of fascinating questions: Why did Rome so utterly destroy the Etruscan civilization after the expulsion of the Tarquinian dynasty which followed the rape of Lucrece? Was it merely the force of destiny, the fatality of events? Or—one dares to ask—was it the vengeance of republican Rome that found bitter pleasure and satisfaction in destroying everything that might recall to the Roman people the undeniable fact that the origins of their very city and all their institutions—laws, army, religion and the civic life itself—had come to them from the Etruscans?

Virgil, in the *Aeneid,* the immortal poem that he composed in exaltation of his patron the Emperor Augustus, to give poetical substance to the legend of the divine ancestry of the Julian family, deftly glossed over many facts concerning the Etruscan origins of Rome. But what Livy and Varro and Dionysius of Halicarnassus revealed to us has been confirmed by modern archaeology after thirty centuries.

Yet the fact remains that the Etruscan civilization had

11

already disappeared two centuries before our era, and next
to nothing was known of it until the earth disclosed the
secrets of the Etruscan tombs. Not one single city or temple
or house remained of what had been the dominant power
in pre-Roman Italy. But the Etruscans had built vast cemeteries underground, which were, in a pictorial sense, the
replica of their houses and cities—and in the last thirty years
the Etruscan civilization has again come to light, with mar-
vels of art and of scientific progress that are no less stupendous than those of Athens and Carthage in their splendid
days.

Many things, however, remain shrouded in mystery. Who
were the Etruscans? Where had they come from? What language did they speak?

To the first two questions the historians have provided
some acceptable answers; but the language remains indeci-
pherable. No new Rosetta stone, that enabled Champollion
to interpret the incomprehensible Egyptian hieroglyphs, has
given the key to a language whose alphabet was the Greek of
archaic times written, however, not from left to right as
Greek itself was written, but from right to left like an Oriental language and with such a paucity of vocals as to frus-
trate any attempt to solve its mystery.

It is said that the Emperor Claudius who, as a prince, had
enjoyed the reputation of being something of an antiquarian,
composed, under the supervision of Livy, a work in twenty
books on the Etruscan antiquities. Undoubtedly he was at-
tracted by the Sibylline Books composed, like everything else
of antiquity in Rome, by the Etruscans, but unfortunately
Claudius' work was lost to posterity.

Etruria was a very small territory—barely 125 miles from
north to south, less than ninety-five from east to west. But
that small area became the birthplace of Italian history.

The achievement of the Etruscans was to have resisted
assimilation, and to have crystallized in their political institutions, their attitude to life, their way of thinking, their culture and their art, the old Mediterranean spirit. By rendering

it deeper, by nourishing it with what could strengthen it
without deforming it, the Etruscans evolved a civilization
that was both brilliant and yet opposed to the Greco-Latin
culture. Without the Etruscan civilization the Latin culture
would never have existed and triumphed, for Rome was the
offspring of Etruria and the successor to the Etruscan herit-
age. It was indeed Etruria that gave to Rome the very conception of her destiny; and according to the ancient tradition,
Rome was to last "one great year," that is, twelve unequal
Etruscan centuries.

It leaves the modern mind amazed how near the truth was
that Etruscan prophecy! The history of Rome is bound to
the Etruscan science of divination in its great moments: the
death of Caesar, for example, the bloody assassination of the
dictator that was to mark the beginning of the ninth Etruscan
century and of the new century of Rome. One hundred days
before the dictator's death, lightning struck the base of his
statue destroying the C in the name Caesar, and an Etruscan
haruspex (soothsayer) was consulted about the meaning of
this omen. The diviner answered without hesitation that the
omen meant that within one hundred days, C—the dictator
—would sit among the gods, which in the Etruscan language
were called Aesar.

Yet, long before Caesar's day, Etruria had suffered at the
hands of Rome the same fate as Carthage. The bitterest
enemy of Rome, defeated in war, Etruria after her defeat
was systematically and pitilessly destroyed; a terrifying example of a merciless democratic vengeance, that was not
satisfied by destroying cities and houses but even had the
name of Etruria decried by the Roman historians and by
Latin moralists anxious to magnify their city. But Etruscan
civilization and art lived on; and when Etruria was already
finished the Emperor Augustus, conscious of the precious
support that the Etruscan doctrine gave him in his endeavor
to keep exotic cults and religions out of Rome, ordered that
the books of the Sibyls be deposited and preserved in the

Temple of Apollo where the very statue of the god was made by an Etruscan artist!

Today the world is greatly interested in the Etruscans. Exhibitions of Etruscan art and jewelry have been held, in the last few years, in Zurich, Milan, Paris, The Hague, Oslo, and Cologne; and the Italian archaeologists are doing great work, both with the spade and historical exegesis. The region of ancient Etruria may soon become a favorite ground for travelers, curious and eager to look at this long-forgotten civilization.

Curiosity about Etruria is not a new thing. In the eighteenth century there was a fashion for Etruscan art. But the craze for digging can be said to have started one evening in 1828 when the Princess of Canino, wife of Luciano Bonaparte, appeared at the Vatican court wearing the delicate Etruscan jewelry that some peasants had found while farming a field in her estates of Bracciano. All the Roman aristocracy who owned land in that region took to excavating. The Prince of Canino had his peasants digging thoroughly, and in two years he made an enormous fortune out of the tombs of Vulci, for the greater part of the jewelry and other treasures found their way to France, England and Germany. The Etruscan fashion was launched: Prosper Mérimée wrote his *Vase Etrusque.*

Today, the work of the archaeologists is done with all the refinements of modern science, with special equipment, by means of a specially devised potentiometer which reacts in different ways according to the obstacles and spaces it encounters, and the center of a tomb having been gauged as exactly as possible, the tufa stone is bored with an electric sounding apparatus until the cavity beneath is reached, and a camera equipped with an electronic flash takes the preliminary pictures showing the conditions of the tomb. All this sounds so "Atomic Age" that one is glad to learn that when the access, or *dromos,* to a tomb is identified, the archaeologists go into action carrying the traditional pick and ax of archaeologists of former times.

It is fortunate that the history of the Etruscans was, in their later period, indissolubly linked with the early history of Rome, for the Roman and Sicilian historians have furnished us with a guiding lamp and a safe ground of comparatively contemporary sources.

To the onlooker who revisits Etruria in search of inspiration, the sight of the buried Etruscan civilization is absolutely fascinating. The Etruscans loved to preserve an enigmatic exterior; enigmatic are their inscriptions and enigmatic to us still remain their divinatory practices that were the *disciplina* of their life. The landscape lends itself to the suggestion; indeed, it is an integral part of the evocation—it is the décor of the drama. I like to think of that landscape as being as old as the reopened cemeteries and tombs that are disclosing to us the life of the Tarquins of twenty-six centuries ago. Latin writers and poets, in later centuries, always spoke of what had been the Etruscan cities as being traversed by the suggestive avenue of bronze-colored cypresses such as the cypresses that one sees today, tall, majestic, somewhat tragic trees, the very trees of a country and of men who made a religion of the haruspical science, still mounting guard upon the necropolis of a people whose civilization has been completely buried, and yet timelessly lives again in our imagination.

And the life of Tarquin the Proud—about which the paucity of sources discouraged Plutarch from writing one of his inimitable lives—is nevertheless the story of the birth of the Roman Republic, one could say of modern democracy.

G. M. F.

BOOK ONE

ALMOST
A
MYTH

I

In 632 B.C., the year 121 of Rome and the eighth year of the reign of King Ancus Marcius, there arrived in the city a prince from Etruria. Laborers working on the slopes of Mount Janiculum said that they saw, in the early hours of the morning, a rich carriage reach the top of the hill arriving at great speed from the other side: the horses had suddenly appeared surging upward from nowhere, two black fiery steeds beating the ground with their hoofs. Then the carriage had come to a standstill upon the very crest of the hill. A man of commanding figure stood up, gazing from that altitude upon the city spread down below within the circle of the surrounding seven hills. Next to the stranger there appeared to be seated a lady; and all of a sudden a portent occurred.

No sooner had the stranger retaken his seat on the driving box than a great eagle descended from a cloud, and fluttering over the stranger's head the bird sacred to the Mighty Jupiter took off his cap with great screams, hovered over him for a while and then replaced the cap upon his head.

No omen, the onlookers said, could be clearer. And clear indeed it seemed to the stranger's wife and to the long train of his attendants. The lady, who was well versed in the sci-

ence of celestial prodigies, immediately embraced her lord
and told him that the eagle had been sent by Jupiter to pre-
dict for him a crown by divine right and an eagle-headed
scepter, which he would soon wield in that very city.

With eager eyes the stranger took in the view of the city
as it lay under the steep sides of the three almost isolated
hills, the Capitoline, Palatine and Aventine; three more came
down as spurs from the plain beyond—Quirinal, Esquiline
and Caelian. Below the hill on which he stood curved the
flowing Tiber in an ample bend, its banks clothed with trees,
here and there crossed by a bridge. Across the Latin plain to
the Alban mountains and the great Etruscan states from
which he had come, the long line of hills, the last spurs of the
Apennines, enclosed the plain to the north.

To the stranger the city seemed to be an outpost not yet
opposing the powerful Etruria, but with the promise that
one day it would rise and conquer. The three isolated hills
made it a natural point of defense or of attack toward the
north; no such point of similar vantage was to be seen lower
down the river. From that city astride the Tiber, armies
could one day operate against any combination, could strike
north, east and south simultaneously. And from the sea no
enemy would ever attempt to invade her. He would conquer
this city, without an army, by the power of his mind and of
his destiny: the bird of Jupiter had signified it!

With such high hopes, the stranger and his train entered
the city, and gave his name as Lucius Tarquinius Priscus. He
was of distinguished mien, and as he had brought with him
considerable riches, he was allowed to stay in the city and
permitted to purchase a house.

To claim descent from the ancient and most famous Tarquinian House, founders of Tarquinia and the all-powerful
Etrurian dodecapolis, was somewhat boastful on the part of
the stranger, for his father's name was Demaratus, a Corinthian who had fled from a charge of sedition and had happened to settle at Tarquinia. Demaratus had married an

Etruscan lady of the Tarquinian family, and at his death his only surviving son had inherited all his property.

The son of Demaratus had married Tanaquil, a lady descended from a very high family,[1] and a woman who would not readily brook the station into which she had married to be inferior to that in which she had been born. The lady Tanaquil soon made a Tarquinius of her husband; and as the Etruscans somewhat despised her Lucius—or Lucumo, as in the Etruscan style he was called—because he was sprung from a foreign settler, she urged him to leave Tarquinia and seek his fortune elsewhere. Rome, the new city, seemed particularly promising for the purpose, as in a newly founded state where all nobility was recent and the result of merit, there would be room for a man of ambition and determination.

The omen on the Janiculum had filled Tanaquil with joy.

Tarquinius was a man of affable address, courteous in his manner and most able to ingratiate people by kindness. Soon a report of him reached the palace; and by paying court to King Ancus with dignity and polite address, in a short time he established himself on a footing of intimate friendship, and became the King's trusted adviser. Land was given to him on the other side of the river Anio; and he was elected to the Senate. His nephew Egerius and all his kindred were received in Rome with honor, and soon Lucius Tarquinius became the King's counselor and his general in the field. Eventually the King appointed him guardian to his children.

---

[1] Livy, *Ab Urbe Condita*, I, 34.

II

Rome was 121 years old, not a great age for any city and merely a fledgling compared with Tarquinia and the other Etruscan cities. In the eyes of Tarquinius Rome was, indeed, a very mean city.

The absurdity of it, the only saving point of the whole situation, was that Rome was the latest, and certainly not the best, of the Etruscan cities outside the federation.

Tarquinius soon learned to keep his counsel on this sore point; although the older families were loath to admit it and spoke hotly of their Latin birth, and even mentioned mythical origins for their city, the only credible founder of Rome was Romulus, an Etruscan. As for his being descended from Aeneas, son of Anchises the Trojan and of Venus, it was nothing but a poetical fable.

At the time of Aeneas' arrival on the Etruscan shores, the Etruscans were already a wealthy and powerful nation by land and by sea, and their fame was known throughout the length and breadth of Italy. The Etruscans were ruling Italy before the Romans were thought of, and the very appellations of the seas surrounding Italy showed the vast power of the Etruscan people.

Romulus, twin brother of Remus, was a grandson of Numitor, and his mother, Rhea Sylvia the vestal virgin, belonged to the family of the Sylvii and was herself related to Numitor, a king of Alba, whose pasture lands, in their day, reached down to the Tiber where their territories joined those of the Sabines and Etruscans, with both of whom they were on equal terms politically. Alba was built three hundred years before Rome, so that this ancient fanum of the Latins, plainly an Etruscan city, and the great temple of Jupiter Latialis, where every year the chiefs from the Latin cities met to sacrifice, was built in a similar style to the Etruscan temple at Voltumna.

The twins Romulus and Remus, children of a sinful affair of the vestal Rhea Sylvia with the God Mars, were brought up at Gabii, under the tutorship of Tanquitius the Etruscan, who was head of the chief college there. And when, all mythical trimmings pruned away, the two brothers decided to found their own city, Rome was built in strict accordance with the Etruscan ritual.

Romulus and Remus had argued about the site upon which the city was to be built, Romulus choosing what was called Roma Quadrata and Remus preferring a ground on the Aventine hill, well fortified by nature, which from him was called Remonium and later on Rignarium.

At last the two brothers resolved to decide their contest by divination. Having placed themselves apart at some distance, Remus saw six vultures and Romulus double that number: the vulture was a bird of good omen, joyful to Hercules and pernicious neither to corn, fruit tree nor cattle, never killing or hurting any living thing and never touching a bird, not even a dead one.

But Romulus had not actually seen twelve birds, and Remus was much incensed; and when Romulus was casting up his ditch, Remus turned the work to ridicule, and to show his contempt he leapt over it. Some said that Romulus struck his brother in anger, others said that Remus was hit by Celer, one of Romulus' companions. Remus fell; in the scuffle another of his companions, Faustulus by name, was also slain; Celer fled into Tuscany, and from him all swift-footed men came to be called Celeres. Romulus buried his brother Remus on the Remonium; and then he resumed building his city. And the first thing he decided was to send for Etruscan priests, to direct him in all the ceremonies and religious rites to be observed.

First, Romulus dug a circular ditch to mark what would be the market place, or comitia, and the first fruits of everything that is reckoned good or necessary were cast into the ditch; and then each of the assembled citizens threw into it a handful of earth.

The ditch was called Mundus; that was the Etruscan way of calling the enclave or universe of men's civic life. Around this Mundus the city was marked out. With a plow fitted with a bronze blade, yoked to a bull and a cow, Romulus drew a deep furrow around the boundaries, the bull and cow being a symbol of fecundity and meaning that man and wife should always labor together for the prosperity of their family and the welfare of their city. And the settlers followed the plowman, turning all the clods raised by the plow inward to the city, and not letting any remain outward, thus implying that the walls should never be destroyed. The furrow described the compass of the city, and between it and the walls was marked the space reserved for the pomerium, or holy space, as lying within and without the city wall.

Romulus marked the gates by taking the plow out of the ground and leaving a break for the gate; this meant that the whole wall was sacred excepting the gateways, as it would be deemed unlawful to carry through the wall anything considered unclean. And in all this Romulus was advised by the Etruscan augur, according to the written rules for the sacred mysteries.[1] The augur had held in his hand the lituus,[2] a small crooked staff without knots, and standing apart from the crowd had drawn with the lituus lines in the air in the

---

[1] Plutarch, *Romulus.*
[2] Livy, Book I, 18.

form of a quadrilateral cross, due north and south, east and west, and he had marked upon the ground the point where the lines crossed each other. Then, the augur and his priests had sat down upon the spot, and covering their heads had waited for some manifestation of the will of the gods. At length, the looked-for sign was given, twelve large birds appearing upon the right hand—twelve vultures, the Egyptian bird of victory. This meant that the city of Romulus would have twelve saecula of dominion: in a similar way Jupiter had intimated to the Etruscans their dominion for ten saecula, or 1,100 years, an Etruscan saeculum averaging 110 years, which they called by the Hebrew term of "one day," the one day of prosperity and rule.[1]

Thus Rome was founded by Romulus the Etruscan, in the true Etruscan manner; it was the twenty-first of April, in the sixth Olympiad.

When the city was built, Romulus divided his citizens again according to Etruscan tradition and rule. All that were of age to bear arms he enlisted into military companies, each consisting of three thousand infantry and three hundred cavalry. These companies he called "legions"; the rest of the multitude was called "the people." One hundred eminent citizens were chosen as counselors, and these he styled "patricians." Their assembly was the Senate, which signified the council of elders. The patricians, some said, were so called also because they were the fathers of lawful children; or because they themselves could tell who their own fathers were, which not everyone of the rabble that poured into a new city at first could do.[2]

In the fourth month after the city was built, Romulus, on the advice of the elders, sent ambassadors to the neighboring states to solicit an alliance and the privilege of intermarriage for his subjects. But nowhere did the embassy obtain favor-

---

[1] This prophecy was current amongst the Rasena, and is often found in Latin writers.

[2] Plutarch—*Vita Romuli.*

able hearing. Perhaps it was a mistake on the part of Romulus to approach first of all the Latin group of cities: but he felt that an immediate alliance with the states outside the Etruscan federation would be a wise move.

The Roman youth resented the rebuff bitterly, and the matter began to point toward violence. Romulus dissembled his resentment and purposely prepared games in honor of Neptune Equestrian, and invited to them all the neighboring peoples. The whole multitude of Sabines came with their women and children. On the preceding day the visitors were hospitably invited to the principal houses, and the Sabines were astonished that the Roman power had increased so rapidly.

On the day of the games, Romulus sat in the front row amidst his nobles, clad in purple: the plan was that when King Romulus rose and gathered up his robe and threw it over his body, his men would draw their swords and fall on the Sabines with a great shout and ravish the most beautiful daughters.

So it happened: when the spectacle was at its height, at the given signal a tumult began, and the Roman youths carried off the Sabine girls by force. Men from the common people, who had been charged with the task, carried to their houses some women of surpassing beauty, reserved for the leading senators. One, far distinguished beyond the others for figure and beauty, was carried off by the party of a man called Thalassius, and in order that no one might molest her while they were carrying her they cried out that she was being taken to Thalassius: from this circumstance the expression became a nuptial one.

It was said that only thirty Sabine girls were taken, and from them the curiae, or fraternites, were named; but in fact more than six hundred girls had been that day abducted, and the only amelioration that Romulus could offer was that they had taken no married women, save one, Hersilia, and she had been taken by mistake. Anyway, the intention of the Romans was simply to form alliance with their neighbors

by the surest bonds, which were those of marriage. Hersilia,
Romulus himself married, and she bore him two children—a
daughter who, by reason of primogeniture, was called Prima,
and one son, whom, from the great concourse of citizens that
came to proffer him congratulations, Romulus called Aollius,
but later Abillius.

The Rape of the Sabines was committed on the eighteenth
day of the month *sextilis,* or August. The minds of the rav-
ished girls were soon quite soothed; but their parents, by
wearing mourning, roused the states; and the Sabines began
a war of revenge. It proved most formidable, as the Sabines
did not make a show of war before they actually began it,
and to prudence they added stratagem.

When the war had lasted nearly four years, the Sabines
advanced at last into Roman territory. Tarpeius was entrusted with the defense of the Roman citadel upon the
Capitoline Hill. The Sabines' king, Titus Tatius, made a
great display of the golden bracelets which he and his officers
wore on their left arms, and Tarpeia, the daughter of the
Roman captain, coveting those exquisite ornaments, betrayed
the fort into the Sabines' hands.

In the night Tarpeia opened one of the gates to let the
Sabines enter. But Tatius was like Antigonus, who loved
would-be betrayers but hated those who had betrayed; and
so he took his bracelet off his arm and threw it at Tarpeia
together with his heavy buckler, and commanded his men
to do the same: Tarpeia was soon buried under the mass of
golden bracelets and bronze shields, and died under the
weight of them.[1] The traitress Tarpeia was buried on the
spot of her crime; and from her the rock was forever called
Tarpeian, and from it were cast to their death all malefac-
tors.[2]

The war with the Sabines came to an end only when, after
many cruel battles, the very daughters of the Sabines, whose
rape had been the cause of the war, came running with cries

---

[1] Livy, *Ab Urbe Condita* I, 11.
[2] Plutarch, *Vita Romuli.*

of misery in the midst of the army, some holding their young babes in their arms, their hair loose, all calling upon their husbands and fathers with the most tender and endearing words.

A truce was thus made, and conditions were agreed, that the women might stay where they were, exempt from all drudgery and labor but spinning; that Romans and Sabines should inhabit the city together, and the city be called Rome, from Romulus, and as a compliment to the Sabines all the citizens should be called Quirites, from Cures the city of Tatius; and that Romans and Sabines should both govern and command together. The place of the ratification was called Comitium.

The population of Rome was thus doubled in numbers; one hundred Sabines were elected senators and the legions increased to six thousand foot and six hundred horse. The people were divided into three tribes: the first, from Romulus, was named Ramnes; the second from Titus Tatius, Tities; and the third Luceres, from the lucas, or grove, where the asylum stood to which people fled for sanctuary and were received into the city. Each tribe contained ten curiae, and the thirty curiae were given the names of the Sabine girls. New rites were instituted, the Matronalia, in honor of the women who had ended the war, and the Carmentalia, in honor of the deity Carmenta who presided over childbirth— although some say that Carmenta was a prophetess, wife of Evander the Arcadian, and because she delivered her oracles in verse, carmen, she was called Carmenta.

Another new rite was the Lupercalia, a feast of purification, for it was solemnized on the *dies nefasti,* or evil days of the month of February, and originally the day of the feast was called Februator. Goats were killed, then two young patricians stained their foreheads with the bloody knife, which others wiped off with wool dipped in milk, and the two young men must laugh after their foreheads were wiped. That done, having cut the goats' skins into thongs, they ran about the streets naked, with only a girdle around their loins, lashing all they met; and the young married women believed that the strokes gave them fertility.

Romulus was the first to consecrate holy fire to Vesta, and he appointed—in the Etruscan manner—sacred virgins to keep the fire burning. Romulus was skilled in divination, for he had been trained by Etruscan masters; and he always carried the lituus, the crooked rod with which the soothsayers described the quarters of the heavens when they sat to observe the flight of birds.

He made the Romans adopt the Etruscan calendar, and instituted laws about marriage, one of which was rather severe, forbidding a wife to leave her husband but granting the husband power to turn away his wife, either for poisoning his children or counterfeiting his keys or for adultery. But if the husband wanted to send away his wife for other reasons, such as her failure to bear him children, he must give to the wife one half of his estate, the other half to fall to the Goddess Ceres. Whoever cast off his wife was to make atonement by sacrificing to the gods of the dead. The wedding ceremony consisted in the imposition of a veil upon the heads of the bride and bridegroom; then the veil was folded upon their two heads to signify the eternity of their union.

Romulus won the war over the Veientes; but this was the last battle Romulus ever fought, for afterward he grew haughty and arrogant. He took to dressing in crimson, with a purple-bordered robe over it; gave audience lying upon a couch of state, always having about him some of his three hundred bodyguards called celeres; and whenever he went about the city the guards walked before him with staves to clear the way, with leather thongs tied around their bodies to bind whomever the King commanded. And when, after the death of his grandfather Numitor in Alba, the throne of that state devolved upon Romulus, and he, to court the Alban people, put the government into their hands, some of the leading men in Rome spoke of seeking a free government, as the patricians were no longer admitted to the state's affairs but only in name, convening in council rather for fashion's sake than to proffer advice.

Things were at this stage when, suddenly, Romulus disappeared and was never seen again. It was the nones of the month Quintilis, or July: Romulus was that day reviewing the army before the assembled people, in the plain near the lake of Capra. Suddenly a great storm arose, with thunder and lightning; the King seemed to be enveloped in a dense mist, and after this Romulus was never seen again on earth. The strangeness was that the senators did not permit the people to make a search, but commanded them to honor and worship Romulus as one taken up to heaven among the gods.

A few days later, while some were accusing the patricians of a misdeed, a faithful friend of Romulus came from Alba, and presenting himself in the Forum and taking the most sacred oath, he asserted that as he was traveling on the road he had seen Romulus coming to meet him, looking taller and comelier than ever, dressed in a shining and flaming armor, and the King had told him: "It pleased the gods, O Proculus, that we who come from them should remain such a long time amongst men as we did; and having built a city to be the greatest in the world for empire and glory, should again return to heaven. Farewell, and tell the Roman people that by exercising temperance and fortitude they shall attain the summit of human power; we will be to you the propitious God Quirinus." [1]

This seemed quite credible to the Romans; and laying aside all jealousies, they prayed to Quirinus and saluted him as a god; and ever since, on the nones of July, the people of Rome went to sacrifice at the Goat's Marsh, shouting some of the ancient Roman names, such as Marcus, Lucius, Gaius, and imitating the way in which the people had fled and cried the day that Romulus disappeared.

Romulus had lived fifty-four years and reigned thirty-eight.

---

[1] Plutarch, *Vita Romuli.*

There were three more kings before the time of the Tarquins; but the history of Rome in those early times is rather confused, and it is difficult to prune the mythical from the tree of real events.

The very alternating of a Sabine king with a Roman one was probably a sign of weakness and indecision within the people. Numa Pompilius, who succeeded Romulus, was celebrated for his justice and piety. He was the youngest of the four sons of Pomponious, an illustrious person of Cures in the Sabine state and he was born on the twenty-first day of April, the birthday of Rome. He was endued with a soul exceptionally tempered by nature and disposed to great virtue, which was increased by discipline, a severe life and the study of philosophy.

When the ambassadors of Rome came to offer Numa the throne he was about forty years of age. He declined. His answer was that "every alteration of a man's life is dangerous to him, but madness only could induce one who needs nothing and is satisfied with everything to quit a life to which he is accustomed. Romulus had the advantage of being thought divinely born and miraculously preserved and matured. My birth was mortal; I was reared and instructed by men that are known to you. The very points of my character that are most commended mark me as unfit to reign—love of retirement and of studies inconsistent with business, a passion that has become inveterate in me for peace, for unwarlike occupations and for the society of men whose meetings are but those of worship and of kindly intercourse. I should be, methinks, a laughingstock, while I should go about to inculcate the worship of the gods, and give lessons in the love of justice and the abhorrence of violence and war to a city whose needs are rather for a captain than for a king." [1]

And yet, was it not rather comical that during his reign he should take as guidance the advice of his wife Egeria and pass it on as the wisdom imparted to him by a goddess?

And the greatest thing one could recall of the reign of

---

[1] Plutarch, *Vita Numae.*

Tullus Hostilius was the episode of the Horatii (Romans) and Curiatii (Albans), though no one was ever sure to which nation the Horatii and to which the Curiatii belonged! [1]

In the history of those two first centuries of Rome, there must be no doubt that only the Tarquins are real historical characters, and must be conceived in quite a different fashion from the more ancient figures around which the earlier legends have been built, and whose historical existence is due to personification alone.

The more ancient figures—Romulus, Numa Pompilius, Tullus Hostilius, Ancus Marcius, and the Servius Tullius which we will find inserted between the first and the second Tarquin—are mere personifications, representatives of the diverse communities and elements of nationalities that went to compose the city. About them legend and history meet and mingle.

The very names of those ancient kings must be taken as the names of the communities personified, or appellations derived from special conditions which characterized such communities.

These regal figures were disguised, overlaid and distorted by a mass of extraneous details, mythical and fictitious. The explanation of this can be found in the unbounded vaingloriousness that influenced the casting of the early history in later times. In the period when the great historians composed their histories and their annals, the Romans suffered— the expression is permissible—from the vastness of the proportions of their state and city. Theoretically they could still persuade themselves and believe that Rome had once been small; but the realization of the fact in practical detail was beyond them. Thus Rome appeared to them as a metropolis from the time of its foundation; the peasants' fights between neighboring settlements became mighty wars skillfully conducted between powerful states and cities, details and color being provided by the observation and technical knowledge of a later and more advanced age.

---

[1] Livy, I, 24.

And by a unanimous tendency, the later historians made the ancient kings appear as Romans from the outset. The name Roman took its rise originally from one community; but in the course of time it had become an honorable title common to all, and every man desired to pose as a Roman of the old stock. The picture drawn by later hands of the most ancient history of Rome conveys no hint, or at least only the remotest, of the crises through which the city and state must have passed before taking the form in which it became the basis of a common life and activity to all elements of the community. This false patriotism of priests and historians was chiefly responsible for the falsification of earlier history—and the most blatant aspect of it was the omission of the vital importance and influence of Etruscan civilization in the formation and development of Rome.

III

Herodotus, who was the first author to attempt, about 450 B.C., a history of the Etruscans, tells us that one century after the war of Troy, or five centuries before the foundation of Rome, when the Mediterranean shores still echoed with the deeds of Ulysses, a colony of people from Lydia, their country being afflicted by a grievous famine, departed from their native land under the guidance of their king's son Tyrsenus and went out over the seas to seek new lands. The venturesome Lydians first went to Smyrna, where they constructed vessels, loaded them with furniture and useful implements, and after skirting several countries they landed on the Tyrrhenian coast, which was then called Umbria of Italy.

Thus Herodotus; but was the land of origin really called Lydia? Smyrna, at that age, did not exist: perhaps Tyrsenus was not a Lydian name. Yet the story is repeated by Strabo, Velleius Paterculus, Virgil, Horace and Plutarch, all deriving their information from the Father of History.

Hesiod and Homer had called them "the mighty Tyrseni," and said that they lived in the days of the demigods.[1] Later on the Greeks called them Turrheni or Pelasgi, and for the Latins they were Etruri, Etrusci or Tusci. But they, the Etrus-

---

[1] Hesiod, *Theogony*, 1015.

34

cans, called themselves Rasenna; and the descendants of the most ancient families always believed that the Rasenna had come from the great and ancient city of Resen or RSN, the capital of Aturia in the land of Assyria situated on the great river Tigris.[1]

Some colonies from Resen had dwelt for a long time in Egypt. They had settled in Egypt at the time when many Asiatic peoples invaded the lands in the southern parts of the Pharaohs' kingdom, about 2500 B.C., wild Scythians and Arabians, trading Edomites and Canaanites, civilized Phoenicians and Assyrians. The Egyptians called them all by the contemptuous name of Hyksos, which meant shepherd race: but the scientific Assyrians had been the architects of the pyramids of Cheops and Cephrenes,[2] and foremost among them were the Rasenna, who flourished peacefully, ruling over various towns one of which was Eluthya, and among the people buried at Eluthya was a great warrior and scribe, named Ranseni, or Rasenna, and also there was Phipe, a frequent Etruscan name sometimes written Fipe or Vipe-na. And in those tombs at Eluthya there were representations of a two-horsed chariot, and a man in the act of writing, and of music and dancing and agricultural work and implements, such as were depicted later in the Etruscan tombs. Moreover, in the country of Ethiopia, where the Pharaohs had granted lands to a group of no less than 240,000 Rasennas, they built the town of Esar—that was, as we have already mentioned, the Etruscan word for demigod. And among the names recorded in the ancient papyri were Pursenna, Mutius and Tages; and above all the name Tarchun, the name of the founder of Etruria. From Egypt they had brought many of their sacred rites; for many centuries they used to place Egyptian things and implements in their tombs.[3]

---

1 Strabo, XVII.

2 Herodotus, ii, 125.

3 They were found in a tomb at Vulci, by the Prince of Canino. And a large scarab of emerald found at Chiusi, although of Etruscan form, shows an engraving of a purely Egyptian subject, a grove of Lotus and Isis giving suck to Horus.

The Rasenna had also lived in Ludin or Lybia and in the Syrtes, until they were chased, as Asiatic, by the Pharaoh; and thus they had at last sailed forth to seek new lands in Italy, about five centuries before the foundation of Rome.[1]

They had arrived in ships fitted for long voyages, for they well understood navigation; and they had brought the arts and sciences that were so well advanced in the East; and they had an oriental love of music, dancing and feasting, pomp and ceremony, dress and show. They were cultivated and refined conquerors; inclined to love easy and luxurious living, with a profound respect for rank and age, a love of order and a religion based on a highly developed art of divination.

Their language was, originally, Assyrian or Phoenician, and their alphabet the one used by that vast continent which lies between the Mediterranean and the Indus, an alphabet not dissimilar to the early Greek, but written in the oriental way, from right to left.

They had first settled in the country between the Apennines and the lower seas, afterward sending colonies north and south, conquering the Umbrians and the Pelasgi. And all the progress of the Rasenna in their new Italian lands and all their institutions and present organizations were the creation of their founder, Tarchun.

Tarchun! His name ranks with the greatest heroes of the ancient world; for he was one of the greatest lawgivers. Through Tarchun the ancient civilization of Asia and the arts and sciences of the East came into Italy. To him Italy owed her knowledge of civil and military life, her skill in seafaring, in agriculture, in road-making, the rules of architecture, the draining of waters, the working of mines, the coinage, the calendar, the refinements of arts, and the doctrines of religion and the ceremonial of worship.

When Tarchun had come to the Tyrrhenian shores, Italy was called Heraclea, Saturnia, Hesperia and also Ausonia. In

---

[1] According to Varro and Cicero, about 1250 B.C.

the south there was a big island, which was called Sikellia. The center of Italy was Uitellia or Vitellia, from a goddess of those parts—the Vitellia of Tarchun became Italia.

But was, perhaps, the country without name? What were the derivations of Heraclea and Saturnia if not from Hercules and Saturn? And where had Hercules and Saturn come if not from the Phoenicians, and who had ever heard of them in Italy until introduced by the Rasenna? Tarchun had brought Hercules' worship into Italy—the Tyrrhenian Hercules, or the strength and power of the Turrheni, of whom Tarchun was the head. There was no image more common on the Etruscan terracotta vases and vessels than that of Hercules, or Erkle. And in the Etruscan mythology he was the husband of Minerva—expressing that absolute perfection which is the union of wisdom with strength.

Tarchun had landed on the west coast of Italy. His first city he had named Tarquinia, and decreed that it should bear his name forever and be, from the first, the seat of government and the capital of all Etruria.

That Tarchun had landed peacefully is quite certain: first, because the tradition does not speak of any opposition on the Rasenna's first appearance, or of any battle and victory which, had it taken place, they would naturally have kept in remembrance by some pillar or monument; second, because all Phoenician colonies seemed to have been established with the goodwill of the natives. Although the ships of Egypt were, at that period, navigating the Mediterranean, Tarchun's ships were the first ever seen on the western coast of Italy, for all the peoples of Italy attributed to the Etruscans the invention of the prow.

Tarchun had founded his city—Tarquinia—with the ceremony used for the foundation of all Etruscan cities, marking out its limits with a bronze plow, which he drove himself.[1] Tarchun's plow was for many centuries held sacred by the Etruscans.

---

[1] There is, in the Jesuit Museum in Rome, an ancient bronze representing this scene and giving us the form of the plow, which never afterward varied.

Tarchun took care that none of his acts should seem to be arbitrary, and therefore he affected to proceed under divine inspiration, and afterward he had his forms and ceremonies written down, that they might serve as the laws of his people to the furthermost posterity.

Cicero records [1] that while Tarchun was plowing the foundations of its walls, a genie arose from the deep furrow, with an old man's head and a child's body; and this genie sang to Tarchun the unalterable, divinely inspired laws of his future government: then the genie sank down and disappeared.

The genie was Tages, a son of Jupiter; the same as the Phoenician Tauatcs and the Egyptian Thoth, the deified writer and lawgiver of the wisest of nations. And Tages, the emblem of the governors and the governed, had the head of a wise old ruler and the body of an innocent child.

Tarchun received the genie in his arms; learned the laws which the divine creature delivered to him in verse, and then he wrote them down.[2] When he had thus written down the laws, Tarchun called around him the chiefs and princes of his people; he recounted to them the wonderful events, and read to them the laws of Tages.

They were laws such as the Rasenna had always revered and respected; but now they sang them with Tarchun and wrote them down; and each ruler of each new city made them their unchangeable laws. For they knew that without a religious sanction human laws can have no stability; and no wisdom was worthy of reverence but what came from above.

They were the Laws of Tages, so wonderful in their content as to have indeed come from heaven. They decided the manner of dividing and classing the Etruscan people, a division that continued throughout Etruria and was adopted by all other cities under Etruscan influence.

The Laws of Tages—or of Tarchun—were written in three volumes, and though many others were added afterward in

---

1 *De Divinitate.*
2 Cicero and Censorinus.

the same spirit, none were held in equal honor. The three books were called the *Libri Fatales,* the *Libri Tagetici,* the *Sacra Acherontica.* The last named was known to Homer, and from his description Sophocles placed Avernus in Tyrsenia.[1]

And when all the laws were written in the books, Tarchun introduced augury, and since that day augury and divination were called Ars Etrusca and Disciplina Etrusca.[2]

In Homer's time the Etruscans were already masters of the Italian seas, which other nations knew only by name. But Tarchun had no knowledge of Greece and no communications with it, as the earliest settlement of Greeks in Italy came more than one hundred years after Tarchun's death.[3]

Tarchun laid his roads throughout Etruria, with the same rule of straight lines which he had used to lay his camps and his cities and his temples; and he had the example of the highways and the canals of Egypt. The hilly nature of the ground in Italy was no difficulty to Tarchun, who knew how to tunnel through hills, to quarry stones, to divert rivers and to drain lakes. His roads were all paved; dug two feet deep, then a quantity of silaria, or composition of earth and stone ground to paste, was laid upon beams of burnt wood, and over this was placed a layer of basalt.

He then made drains and tunnels and channels for irrigation, which he spread from one end of Etruria to the other. As drainer of the ground and manager of the power of water, he taught his people to surpass all other people in the world,

---

[1] These Etruscan books were translated into Latin in the days of Lucretius, and collected in fifteen volumes, with comments by C. Labeo. Cicero, in *De Divinitate,* quotes from translations of the *Libri Etrusci, Chartae Etruscae, Libri Tagetici, Disciplina Tagetis, Sacra Tagetica,* and the *Liber Terra ruris Etruriae.* Pliny says that these books had pictures in them, and Servius states that in the days of the Father of the Gracchi the Augural Books and the *Libri Reconditi* were translated from the Etruscan. To mention one more authority, Festus says that the *Rituales Etruscorum Libri* told of the rites for consecrating altars, temples, cities, walls and gates and of the levying of armies and the government of people.

[2] Ovid, in the *Metamorphoses,* says that Tages was the first who taught the Etruscans to see into the future.

[3] Cuma, the oldest Greek colony in Italy, was founded about 1060 B.C. and for a long time it was a small obscure place without any trade.

excepting only the Egyptians who had been their masters. Under Tarchun's teaching the Etruscans carried off the water where it was superfluous and increased it by irrigation where the natural supply was short. They knew how water could be managed to increase the riches of their possessions, and to fertilize the lands which, until then, had never been cultivated.

They drained the marshes; they lowered the waters of the lakes and deepened the channels of the rivers and straightened and regulated them. Florence was built on the site of a former lake, and they cut through the Gonfalina rock that shut up the valley of the Arno to make arable the land on each side of the river. They turned the brook Clanis into a river to drain into it the marshes of the Chiana.

They worked the mines, the first mines ever opened in Italy, and their rich ores became an important article of commerce in the hands of the Etruscans. The mines were worked by the government, using slave labor; and when the mines were privately owned they paid a royalty of one-tenth to the state.

Tarchun was the first to introduce the vine into Italy, the cultivation of which he had learned in Egypt. The method followed in Etruria was the same as that described on the tomb of Beni Hassan. And from Egypt too Tarchun brought to the shores of Italy the use of olives.

At the time of Aeneas' arrival, the Etruscans were already wealthy and powerful, not by land only but over the sea, extending the whole length of Italy, which, from the Alps to the Straits of Sicily, was filled with their fame.[1] They ruled practically all Italy, and their dominions extended to the upper and lower seas by which Italy is surrounded; and the very appellations of those seas showed the vast power of the Etruscans, for the Italians called the one Tuscan, from their name, and the other Adriatic from Adria, an Etruscan colony.

---

[1] Livy, I, 2.

The Etruscans had divided their dominions in twelve states, or lucumonies; and, by sending colonies equal in number to the mother cities first on this side of the Apennines to the lower sea and afterward on the other side, they had come to possess all the territory beyond the river Po as far as the Alps, excepting a corner belonging to the Venetians, who dwelt on the sea.[1] In this way, they had conquered Agylla, Pisa, Saturnia, Alsium, Faleria and Fescennium from the aboriginal Pelasgi or Umbrians, whose only traces remained in Cortona and Perugia. Well-nigh three hundred towns had the Etruscans conquered from the Umbrians.

The first conquest had been the region which formed the state of Tarquinia, in the neighborhood of Tarchun's own first city; and the state ever after bore his name and contained within it the holy fanum of the Etruscans, Voltumna, in which they had erected the temple of National Concord and at which they held their yearly parliament. Tarchun had no allies in his first conquest: on and on he had marched for years, and with each town conquered he had increased his force. At the same time, his ships subdued with ease the primitive towns on the seacoast.

He had first marched northward to Pisa, and then he had ascended the river to Fiesole, whence he had turned south to Camerti and Sarsinati. The Umbri fled before him, and were glad to sue for peace with the mighty Rasenna, who offered them a treaty that was just and equitable and was never broken.

Soon the Etruscan dominion extended from the Apennines to the Tiber, and from the Tyrrhenian sea to the confines of Umbria. The Umbrians adopted much of the Etruscan religion and laws and customs, and joined them in their annual worship, and were glad of the privilege of burying their foremost families in an Etruscan necropolis. Throughout the territories the Etruscan language was understood and spoken; and the singular and wise policy of the Etruscans was to give

---

[1] Livy, V, 33.

the conquered peoples a share in the government and an equal interest in the permanence and prosperity of the state, thus nullifying all feelings of humiliation and hostility.

Four centuries before Rome each Etruscan lucumony was settled under its own prince, all ruling according to the Tarquinian laws. Their treaty of peace with Tarquinia was the typical treaty granted by the Etruscans to the Umbrians, and was engraved on the Eugubian tables: "There shall be peace between the contracting powers, the Rasenna and the Umbri, so long as the heavens and the earth retain their places: neither shall attack the other, nor yet suffer the other to be attacked: neither shall raise up enemies to the other, and if one suffer loss, the other shall afford him protection, help and support. They shall share one common danger and divide one common booty; and if cause of complaint arise between them, it shall be decided within ten days in the place where the offense happened. Nothing shall be added to this treaty nor might anything be diminished from it." [1]

The most holy of all Etruscan temples was that of Tinia [2] Tarquiniensis, in Tarchun's own city of Tarquinia where he had been king, priest and augur—a covenant between God and man, and the augur, in those early days, firmly believed that his thoughts and words were inspired.

Tarchun had measured the ground for his temple, choosing it in the highest part of Tarquinia, close to the fortress, in order that one might sanctify and bless while protecting and defending the city. Then Tarchun took his omen, which was a flash of lightning drawn by himself from a cloud—for the augur had a mysterious power over the electric element. The multitude of his people stood reverentially looking at him; and he pronounced his solemn words in the name of Tinia of the Rasenna: "My temple and my sacred land shall

---

[1] This extraordinary document, which might be a lesson of policy to modern nations and governments, is to be found in Dionysius, VI, 95, and is copied by him from the older historian Macer, who declares to have read the treaty and describes the offerings made upon its confirmation.
[2] Jupiter.

extend as far as I please to make it holy and to dedicate it by
the mouth that now speaks. That oak and that oak which I
name shall bound my temple to the east, and that cypress and
that other shall bound my temple to the west. Between them
I limit this temple with the drawing of lines. I survey it with
the sight of mine eyes and I establish it according to my good
will and pleasure." Then Tarchun the augur drew with his
lituus the lines upon the ground, and again in the air, in the
form of a cross. He raised his outstretched hands to heaven,
and then was silent.[1] This was the prayer of consecration.

The four points marked by the lines were the cardinal
points. Each section was again divided into four, so that the
ground occupied by the building contained sixteen points,
each giving its peculiar augury. The northeastern was the
most fortunate, and when the augur officiated or was consulted he placed himself in the position of the gods, who were
supposed to inhabit the north. The most solemn and most
revered consultation was when the augur drew the lightning.
Each point that the lightning touched conveyed a different
meaning. Lightning could answer yes or no; it signified which
god was to be honored or appeased, and testified to success or
defeat. And birds were taken as omens to signify by their
numbers.

When the dedication of the ground for the temple was
completed and the foundations were surrounded with fillets
and crowns, Tarchun called men and soldiers who had happy-
sounding names, and they threw in the enclosed space
branches of olive and other sacred trees. Then came the vestals, who were the virgin sisters of Tarchun; and they bathed
the place with fountain and river water. Thus were the vestal
virgins instituted by Tarchun, a derivation of a religious order founded in Egypt by Queen Nofre-Ari, the Ethiopian
queen of Amenoph the First, in the sixteenth century B.C.
And ever after only virgins of the highest families were admitted among the vestals, who were under the charge of the

---

1 Varro, Tacitus and Plutarch.

king himself as Pontifex Maximus. The virgins were expressly brought up to take charge of the sacred fire, the emblem of pure divinity. They were dedicated from birth, and spent ten years in learning, ten in exercising and ten in teaching their office to the novices; at the age of thirty they were entitled to marry. Their dignity was almost royal. They could reprieve criminals whom they might meet on their way to or from the temple, and when they appeared in public the fasces were carried before them. If the sacred fire which the vestal virgins were obliged to keep always burning should by any accident be extinguished, it must be drawn from heaven again. When this fire was first lighted in Italy, the Etruscans had drawn it from the sun, as an additional consecration of their new country.

Upon the ground of his new temple Tarchun sacrificed a bull, a sheep and a pig, and laying the entrails upon the grass, he prayed to Tinia to bless the place. Then he touched the garlands which bound the sacred cornerstones, and each stone he raised by a cord, while all the people shouted and helped him. Then all threw gold and silver and copper, both raw and worked, and the ceremony was ended.

The building of his temple had been a work of peace; and when it was built he dedicated it, as it would have been reckoned a singular misfortune in his life had he not done so, and his name would not have been inscribed and preserved in front of the temple. Once again he assembled all his lucumons, at the full moon of September which was the beginning of the sacred year, for the civil year began in March. And in the presence of a vast multitude, Tarchun offered a sacrifice. Taking a large nail many inches long, with a great blow he struck it into the side doorpost of the temple. That nail marked the beginning of the Etruscan era; and proclaiming that Tinia had given them the land of the Umbri which they had duly conquered and colonized, he named the whole country Etruria.

From that day forward, a periodical ceremony was to be held at Tarquinia every lustrum, or period of five years, when the September moon was full: and in the presence of the assembled people, the king would strike a new nail into the doorpost of the temple to record that another lustrum had passed.[1] Thus came the fixing of the calendar, properly calculated by the wise men and astronomers.

The dedication of the temple of Tinia Tarquiniensis marked the grand epoch from which the saecula of the Etruscans were ever dated, that is the twelfth century, or precisely 1187 B.C.[2]

Thus Etruria had grown. It was now a powerful and prosperous dodecapolis; but everything remained as it was conceived and ordered by Tarchun in his institutions.

Etruria was a confederation of twelve lucumonies, each constituted by a city and the neighboring territory—Duodecim Populi Etruriae—and Tarquinia was the capital and Voltumna the national fanum.

The other cities were Volcenta (Vulci), Vetaln (Vetulonia), Caere (Cervcteri), Arezzo, Chamars (Chiusi), Roselle, Velathri (Volterra), Cortona, Perugia, Velzu (Volsini) and Pupluna (Populonia).[3]

The Umbrians and Pelasgi were governed as municipia. This was a form of alliance instituted by Tarchun, peculiarly according to the genius of Tagetic faith, which desired each people to preserve its own gods. The municipia had their allotted number of regiments; they had a court of justice of

---

1 Plutarch in *Publicola*.

2 This date brings the closing of the Etruscan era to the year 666 of Rome, or 87 B.C., the time when the Etruscan augur, as mentioned by Plutarch, proclaimed that the end of the national day had come. And the Etruscans alone among the nations of antiquity left a precise date of their origins: their well instructed augur proclaimed that they did not rule Tyrrhenia farther back than 434 years before the foundation of Rome.

3 For the composition of the ancient dodecapolis we have the names of the first three cities on the fragment of a marble throne of the Etruscologue Emperor Claudius, from the Roman theater of Cerveteri (now in the Lateran Museum), upon which are still visible three figures, with the inscriptions *Tarquinienses, Volcentani, Vetulonienses*. For the names of other cities, see Dionysius of Halicarnassus (III, 51), Diodorus Siculus (XX, 35, 5) and Livy (XXVIII, 45).

their own; but as the natives of municipia could not be peers of the realm, they had no vote and no share in making the laws.

The foreign neighbors or allies were called isopolites—isopolity meaning a community between independent states, so long as the subjects of either dwelt in the towns of the other: with the isopolites the state was patron and they were honored guests, to whom complete rights were granted excepting the peerage, and they were welcome to serve in the army.

The cities of the confederation had a monarchical government: the kings were called lucumons, and were chosen from among the highest nobles. The lucumons ruled with the collaboration of the principes, or senators, representatives of the old founders. The lucumo held the judicial power: every eight days there was an audience, at which the king sat in judgment and advised his subjects.

The Etruscan kings had evolved all the ceremonial of magistracy and its symbolism such as was continued forever in Rome: the lictors with the fasces; the trabeae curules, or ceremonial robes; the golden ring indicating the senatorial or knightly ranks; the paludamentum, or red mantle of the commander in chief of the army; the senatorial toga praetexta bordered in purple; the quadriga granted to the triumphing general; the painted togas and the togas embroidered with palms.[1]

The lucumo, when sitting in judgment, was attended by hushers, or apparitors; and the lucumo sat upon a curule chair—sella curulis—that was of ivory and sometimes was gilt, a beautiful and comfortable chair, slightly rounded in the back.[2] Some curule chairs were backless, with crossed legs.

Equally, Tarchun had fixed the pomp of Triumph: the golden diadem for the victor, which was forever called Etrusca corona. The victor was entitled to wear the tunic palmata, decorated with palms, of golden texture; the painted toga; and an ivory scepter topped with an eagle. Around his

---

[1] Annius Florus, I, 5.
[2] For the apparitors and the curule chairs see Livy, I, 8.

neck the victor wore the bulla, which in Rome was called
Etruscum aurum: a golden medallion inside which were minute charms against the evil luck.[1]

Tarchun had devised the symbolism of numbers: twelve
were the lictors surrounding a lucumo. He had also instituted
the feciales, officers whose duty was to take away the reasons
for war and repress the spirit of vengeance, for the Etruscans
as a people found no delight in battles or bloodshed. Tarchun founded colleges of feciales, all men of noble birth, and
their office was sacred; hence their persons, while officiating,
were inviolable. There were several of them in each lucumony, and their character was something between ambassador and herald. If one tribe offended another, the feciales
were sent in ceremonial dress and crowned with vervain, a
plant sacred to the Phoenician god of citadels. They rode in
chariots, drawn by two richly caparisoned horses, and being
admitted into the senate the feciales named the grievance of
which they complained and demanded redress within ten
days, repeating the demand thrice so as to give three truces of
ten days each to the offenders. At the end of this time, if their
representations were not attended to, they took Tinia and the
other gods to witness that they had performed their duty, and
it was now for their country to decide. On their return home,
they informed the senate that war was lawful; and, if war was
resolved upon, they returned to the boundary of the hostile
state, and there cast a spear across the frontier into the enemies' territory.

Not only the feciales, but also the augurs and haruspices
were all of noble birth, the aristocracy of the country. Besides
them there were the lucumons, who formed the standing
council of the sovereign and the hereditary senate. The eldest
sons were not their equals as long as their fathers lived, and
could not fill magisterial offices until they themselves were
created lucumons. The continuance of this order in numbers
was entered in the tombs, and the king, or lar, could fill up

---

1 Juvenal, V, 5. Later in Rome, the *bulla* and the *toga praetexta* became
prerogatives of the young boys of noble families.

the vacancies in his senate occasioned by the extinction of the original great houses.

All the princes of Etruria were potentially lucumons; they were the chief landholders, and in them, as a body, rested the whole power of the state. The head lucumo, or king, was a lar.[1]

Tarchun had commanded that all the lars of Etruria proper should be elected by the lucumons of each state for life; and each king was at the same time Pontifex Maximus in his own dominion, and an absolute ruler when not restrained by law. When he died, his son might succeed him if a plurality of votes so decided; but if the lucumons could not agree, each chief lucumo would rule five days. The king originated every new law and proposed it to the senate, that approved or rejected it, amended it or advised upon it, but could not originate a law.

Equally, the king was the sole judge, with power to absolve or to punish, both in civil and criminal cases. The king appointed all the great officers of state; he was, in fact, head of the nobles, father of the people, protector of the realm, commander of the army and sole declarer of peace and war.

His installation took place after having consulted the gods, and the pontifices examined him as to his fitness for office, because he was himself to be Pontifex Maximus.

The king was then *primus inter pares,* and the entire form of government was a tempered autocracy. The king received property appropriate to his dignity, called demesne lands, and he was entitled to one-third of the spoils of conquered territory in war. He had the care of all public money, and it was his duty, every day following the eighth day, to give audience and to show himself to his people in the porch of the palace or in the forum, to hear complaints, to decide quarrels, to redress grievances, to receive obeisance and salutations, to announce the feasts for the following week and the changes of the moon, which regulated the calendar. These public audiences were patriarchal meetings, and the people greeted

---

[1] From the Hebrew *Sar.*

the king with respect and affection and inquired after his health.

The nobles were compulsorily educated, because to them alone belonged all authority in religious and political matters: the augurs and haruspices who made known the will of the gods must know how to ascertain it; the generals must understand the maxims of war; the senators must be conversant with the laws. The calculators of the new moon and feasts, the keepers of the annals, and the measurers of land must be versed in astronomy and the science of numbers.

Tarchun had formed his original cities of houses or families of princely rank, eleven in number, and the lucumo would be the twelfth and the supreme head. Their followers were vassals or clients or clansmen: indeed, the name derived from CLNs. Each clan, or family, took the name of his chief and formed a gens.

In each Etruscan city there were three tribes, each tribe being represented in the senate by one hundred peers, each peer standing for ten registered houses, of which he was lucumo. These lucumons, or captains, were again divided into groups of ten, each forming a curia, and over each curia was a decurion commanding one hundred warriors. Hence the ten decurions of each tribe were the princes of the senate, whose votes were taken first, and as each of them voted so the nine under them would consider themselves bound to vote.[1]

To counterbalance the lucumonic families, direct descendants of the ancient colonizers, there were the tribes of the plebs, composed of the native people, and to them were added the servants and the slaves acquired by the nobles in outer lands. The three tribes of the senate symbolized all the structure of the Etruscan polity: the three great gods, the three holy gates, the three classes of priests, warriors and peo-

---

[1] We find the same institutions in Rome, from the early times, which proves that they were of Etruscan origin. It is interesting to note that throughout Italian history there was a survival of the "first ten" holding the determining vote in their senates—usually designated as "the Council of the Ten."

ple, with masters, vassals and slaves, which made up the whole nation.

The twelve lucumonies, therefore, at the time of Tarquin, were aristocratic republics. When new laws were made, the senators announced them to the people assembled in centuries, and these centuries were entitled to meet every ninth, or market, day. Each city had a district assigned to it upon its foundation, called *agger,* which was never afterward enlarged and in which were built the suburbs. All the measured land beyond the agger was pasturage and belonged to the senators, for their use and their clans. This land was limited, its boundaries carefully marked and placed under the perpetual care of twelve nobles called *arvales* who represented the twelve Etruscan tribes. On festival days the arvales walked in procession three times around the boundaries, crowned with oak.

Tarchun had also instituted an army with a carefully detailed organization. The house of each curia gave one man to the legion, or one hundred per curia; and each curia gave ten men to the cavalry. Every childless member of the curia left his estate to the curia, for the land could never be alienated; and each curia must supply the same number of men to the army.

The infantry was divided into three ranks: principes, or first men; hastati or spear bearers; and triarii, or third rank. There were also the celeres, or bodyguard of the prince. The three ranks, with the velites, or light spears, and the cavalry, made five classes of troops. The cavalry was divided into bands, or turmae, ten in each row; and each legion comprised three thousand foot and three hundred horse.

Tarchun had laid down some precepts concerning the limits and duties of human life. The life of man, as originally bestowed by Tinia, was to last 120 years: "But [had said Tages to Tarchun] in our degenerate days Fate has abridged man's life to three periods of thirty years each, which, alas! are continually getting shorter. The half of the first period, or fifteen, is the period of childhood, when a noble youth

shall wear around his neck the bulla against the evil eye, because he cannot defend himself. Upon entering his sixteenth
year let him assume the toga, and begin to practice military
exercises, which he shall follow for two full years. At seventeen he shall be eligible for the army and to vote at the polls;
and at twenty-five, but not earlier, he shall be capable of
magistracies and offices of trust. Until forty-five he is bound to
go forth with the host, to fight against an enemy; but from
forty-five to sixty let him stay at home and fight within the
city and defend his own frontiers and his father's home. At
sixty he becomes senex, and all his duties will end, except in
the case of princes and commanders and the equestrian order
in general, who are never held to be past the service of their
country."

The foot regiments wore magnificent helmets of different
shapes, adorned with ostrich plumes; cuirasses, greaves, bucklers of many forms, bows and arrows, spears, javelins, long
broadswords, and short glaves and daggers.

When they were in the field or serving in a garrison, the
soldiers received pay, which was provided by a regular tax, to
which all citizens were subject. The heavily armed soldiers
were taken from among the rich; as they received more booty,
they were expected to arm themselves.

Only the slaves were excluded from entering the army, as
they were a degraded caste; but slaves might be freed and
placed among their owners' clients, when they could serve in
their lord's own regiment.

Tages had transmitted to Tarchun the sacred division of
time for his people, which every lar, lucumo and velthur—
king, governor and magistrate—was to follow and proclaim
to the people at market days. There was the Great Year,
which Tarchun had called a secle or cycle, consisting of one
hundred and ten minor years, divided into twenty-two lus-
trums, or twenty-two periods of five solar years. A lustrum
was the period for which the state lands were let. The minor
years were either civil or sacred. The civil year began in
March and consisted of 365 days, divided into ten months

and two intercalaries; and the sacred year began in September, according to the manner of the Egyptians, and it consisted of ten months only. The ten months of the year were divided into thirty-four weeks, of eight days each, named in numerical order.

The month was divided into two parts by the ides,[1] which corresponded to the full moon. The weeks, of eight days, were called nundinae, or nonae; every ninth day, or nones, was market day. And as no lunar month could be perfectly divided in weeks of eight days, for it should have twenty-four or thirty-two days, in each month there was a residual time, a variable number of days of which the town dweller and especially the peasantry had to take notice in computing the time of their tilling and sowing. Consequently, the calends which marked the division of one month from another, coincided with the day of the new moon, when the Pontifex, invoking Juno to whom the calends were sacred (the ides were sacred to Jupiter), announced whether five or seven were the days to the first nona of the month, according as the month was of twenty-nine days—twenty-four days or three nundinae plus five additional days—or of thirty-one days, that is, twenty-four days or three nonae plus seven additional days. The days after the ides, the calends and the nones were days of bad omen—*atridies:* hence the distribution in the calendar of good omen, or *fas* days, and bad omen, or *atri* days.

The ten-month year was the term of mourning for near relations, of paying portions left by will, of credit for debt, of all money transactions and interest upon capital, and of all truces, treaties and engagements relating to war or military affairs.

And Tarchun had given just laws against crimes, the severest of which was the punishment of parricides. The criminal guilty of such a terrible crime was put into a sack with a mad dog, a viper and an ape and thrown into the river.[2] Homosexuals were thrown into the sea nailed inside a chest.

---

[1] Itis or itus, iduare, meaning to divide.
[2] This punishment was still in force in Rome at the time of Nero. After

Under these laws and institutions the Etruscans had pros-
pered and had become a great nation. The soil of their country was rich in minerals, and the Isle of Elba provided them
with iron. The Etruscan exploited this precious wealth, trans-
porting the extracted ore to the high furnaces at Populonia;
more furnaces were in the island itself, which was called
Aithalia, the ardent. From Elba also came copper; thus the
Etruscans produced a beautiful bronze, for which they imported tin from the Cassiterides, the Scilly Isles southwest of
Britain, bringing it across Gaul to the mouth of the Rhone
and then shipping it to the Etruscan ports. Iron, copper and
bronze were important items of export, both as metal and
manufactured articles. Bronze utensils and vessels from Etruria found good markets in Greece.

Etruria was rich in agricultural products; and to increase
the crops their engineers had built colossal hydraulic works
to drain the marshes and redeem fresh land, cutting tunnels
through the rocky mountains to make drains for the water.
They built sewers in all their towns to provide for the hy-
giene of the dense populations.

The expanding trade and the increasing wealth had developed the system of weights and measures and of coinage.
The original coinage of Tarchun, like every other Eastern
coinage, expressed weight; and the as, or Etruscan pound,
was divided into six parts, each marked with as many dots as
expressed its division—semis, tertiens, quadrans, sextans and
uncia. Upon his coins Tarchun had impressed the prow, in
memory of the ships in which he had reached Italy. The coinage, in silver and gold, was most beautiful, with Minerva on
the face and a running dog or a bull or lion on the obverse
side.[1]

---

the assassination of his mother Agrippina, the Emperor in his nightmares
dreamed of being pursued by the populace and condemned to the fate of
parricides.

[1] The Etruscan coinage, the oldest in Europe, was adopted by all Italy.
No other was known until the year 480 of Rome, when the Romans began
to coin silver.

New industries had been invented. The Etruscan shoes and boots were famous in all Mediterranean countries. In Athens the Etruscan sandals were the height of fashion, especially the style with a thick wooden sole and gilt leathern straps. The ladies' sandals were very soft and of slender design.

Science too had progressed; medicine was highly developed, and dentistry had become a fine art, the Etruscan dentists supplying gold bridges for the mouths of their patients. The dentists had even devised the means of keeping together the teeth of a dead person—*auro dentes juncti*. Doctors had discovered the curative qualities of thermal waters—the Fontes Clusini at Chianciano, the hot baths of the Aquae Populoniae, and many others.

Music was highly appreciated, in public and private entertainments, and Etruscan flautists were eagerly sought in Egypt and in Carthage. Literature was not much developed, for the Etruscans were not a literary people; but there was a national theater, a kind of rustic comedy.

The fame of Tarchun the Founder was so great that popular tradition attributed to him also the towns and cities which were founded or acquired long after Tarchun: Gravisca, in the territory of Tarquinia; Alsium, Fescennium, Aurinia afterward known as Saturnia, and Pisa. These were all conquered Umbro-Pelasgian towns, and around them had been erected the sacred Etruscan walls and gates of square blocks, regularly cut and built without cement.

Now they were all big commercial centers, flourishing under Etruscan rule; but none of them was residence of a sovereign prince or capital of a state, except Falisci. Pisa had been entirely rebuilt by Tarchun, who had constructed a new port in Eastern style, and changed the name of the town in Pisa and made it the Queen of the Arno. Tarchun also conquered from the Umbrians Cortona, Perugia and Camers, whose name he had changed to Clusium. And he founded Luna, on the Gulf of Spezia, and Populonia and Cosa.[1] Veii

---

1 Virgil, Aeneid, X—now called Volterra and Vulci.

was chosen as the site of a border fort, its name meaning a boundary.

Yes, they were great and beautiful cities—Luna of the candid walls; [1] Pisa, the mouth of noisy waters; Fiesole, the tribe on a rock; Volterra, the high fortress, built to keep Pisa in check and for this reason the first genuine Etruscan city after Tarquinia; Vetulonia, the Daughter of the Highest, with its colossal walls, mosaic pavements, beautiful statues, huge amphitheater, and a spa well visited because of the neighboring hot springs; Populonia, a harbor for metals, emporium of the iron and copper ores extracted in the mines of Elba; Arretium, famous for its manufactures of pottery and arms; Cortona, also called Corytus; Perugia, a noble city near the famous Mount Ciminus; Clusium, a rival of Tarquinia in power and ambition; Rusella, the top of the hills, near Lake Castiglione; Volsinia, reputed for the mechanical arts and handmills, hence its name Felsuna meaning the mechanic tribes.[2]

And there were Cosa, Agylla, Pyrgi, Vulci and Veli; and of these, twelve were ruling cities, capitals of lucumonies—Tarquinia, Volterra, Clusium, Cortona, Perugia, Arretium, Falerii, Volsinii, Rusella, Vetulonia, Caere and Veii. The twelve lucumonies composed the federation of Etruria, and each lucumony was protected by the walls that Tarchun built, indestructible walls of great stone blocks, laid together without cement, sometimes in alternate courses and sometimes with one course lengthways and the next endways, all of prodigious thickness and strength, with square towers about fifty yards apart, with lofty gates, either arched or square, and with a citadel and a temple. Each city had a theater, a circus and an amphitheater, and public baths and sewers and drainage.

The architecture was so beautiful and conceived on so vast

---

[1] Rutilius, *Candentia Moenia Lunae.*

[2] The numismatic names of those cities were Piet.he.sa, Pisa; F.lsole, Fiesole; Felathri, Volterra; Fetluna, Vetulonia; Pupulun, Populonia; Felsune, Volsinia; Cisere, Caere.

a scale as to strike the minds of poets and writers. Those cities were the evidence of the wealth, the power, the moral force, the civilization of the Etruscans and only the hand of tyranny could have built them. But the overlords were men of genius, men who loved to magnify their power. Those Etruscan lucumons had a distinction over the other ancient peoples, for there was the greatness of public character stamped upon all their works. Everything they did was for public utility and the benefit of all—the common religion, the common improvements, the common security, the common wealth, the common comfort; and they did it with such a vastness, such a solidity, such a grandeur, such an artistic and scientific skill, that the fame had spread far and wide, to Athens, to Egypt, to mighty Carthage. The public works of Etruria were indeed the glory of Tarchun and the glory of the Tarquinian dynasty, raised by laws imposed upon the citizens as a duty, according to one standard, sacred in the eyes of those who had imparted them and of those who obeyed them.

The Etruscans had entered the maritime competition, urged by their vitality, their irrepressible need of commercial expansion and to obtain raw materials for their crafts and industries. The same ability that had made them create an army that had given them supremacy on land, made them capable of building a fleet that answered all the needs of expansion. They were excellent mariners; their ships had brought to Italy the invention of the prow and the anchor.

It was a pirates' fleet, to be sure, but what was sea trade if not piracy? Piracy was the current money of the Greeks, the Phoenicians, the Carthaginians. The Etruscans proved masters in that art, and became redoubtable. But they kept themselves to the western Mediterranean, the Mare Nostrum that was comprised between the Italian coast and the Pillars of Hercules and the African shore from Libya to Numidia. By not interfering with the Greeks, who had a monopoly of the eastern Mediterranean, the Etruscans cut them out of the western trade.

The control of the western Mediterranean was not without

disputes, for it cut off the Greeks, especially the Samians and Phoceans, from the rich mineral sources of Tartessos in Andalusia, and there had been Greek bases and ports and colonies at Monaco, Marseilles, Barcelona and Valencia. Fearing the inevitable loss of those bases, the Greeks tried to create in Sardinia and in Corsica more solid ones, especially at Alalia on the eastern shores of L'Ile de la Beauté, exactly facing Etruria.[1]

In the year 890 B.C., barely one hundred and thirty-seven years before Rome, and long after the Etruscans had been flourishing on the Tyrrhenian shores, a small colony from Tyre had founded Carthage—Kartaca—on the southern shore of the Mediterranean sea. Utica already was a great and powerful state in Africa. The new settlers received land at no great distance, and with the help of the Libyans they built the citadel of Bursa,[2] although later Carthage consisted of three different parts, Megara, Bursa and Cothon. The territories of Utica and Carthage were divided from Numidia by the river Tusca. Queen Dido, a widowed princess of Tyre, was the founder, and as the city rose near the Barcae, who were Phoenicians like Queen Dido and her settlers, Barca became the name of the princely family.

The Carthaginian nobles were merchants. They consulted the flight of birds and carried images of gods and heroes as figureheads on the prows of their ships, and for a long time they sent every year tithes and offerings to the temple of Hercules at Tyre.

Soon Carthage had acquired great wealth; and the Etruscans became acquainted with the Carthaginians through the Uticans, in the intercourse of sea trade. The ambition of Carthage was to establish herself on the three great islands—Sicily, Sardinia and Corsica. Confronted with this situation, Etruscans and Carthaginians chose the elementary laws of politics: they signed a treaty of peace and amity,[3] and agreed

1 In 565 B.C.
2 Bozrah.
3 In 545–540 B.C., mentioned by Aristotle.

upon respective spheres of influence. In this way they presented a united front against Greek imperialism. The final clash occurred in 540 B.C. between the Phocean fleet and the allied fleets in the waters of Alalia. After the battle, the Greeks took on board their remaining ships all the women and children and what they could load of their goods. They left Corsica and sailed away toward Rhegion. Etruscans and Carthaginians shared the abandoned ships, and the people of Caere took a great number of prisoners and brought them home to Etruria. Then, before the whole city, they took them outside the walls and stoned them to death.[1]

Thus was Etruria in the first half of the second century of Rome at the peak of her power, ruling over the greater part of Italy, sharing with Carthage the domain of the western Mediterranean. And over Carthage she had the advantage of a great continental empire, founded upon the safest and strongest of rules—the federation of her lucumonies.

Rome was but an uncertain entity. An Etruscan city in all but name, restive and ambitious and anxious to assert her own independence, like a child who disowns its father. And the time seemed ripe to redress the course, and bring the city on the banks of the Tiber into line with the Etruscan empire.

---

[1] Herodotus.

BOOK TWO

THE
TARQUINS

I

In the year 138 [1] King Ancus died, after reigning twenty-four years. Tarquinius succeeded to the throne as a matter of course. In fact, Tarquinius diplomatically helped himself.

He had now been in Rome seventeen years, and for many years he had been the trusted counselor of the King and guardian to the King's children. Ancus' sons were approaching the age of puberty, and for this reason Tarquin felt it was imperative that the assembly for the election of a new king should be held without delay.

He sent the late King's sons to hunt, and the assembly being proclaimed, he addressed the meeting.

He said that he did not aim at anything unprecedented, for he was not the first foreigner, but the third, who aspired to the sovereignty of Rome. Tatius had not only been an alien but even an enemy, and yet was made King; and Numa, unacquainted with the city and without soliciting it, had been invited by the Romans to the throne. He, Tarquinius, had come to Rome with his wife and his entire fortune, and in Rome had spent a greater part of that age in which men are employed in civil offices than he had in his own native

---
[1] 615 B.C.

country. He had both in peace and war thoroughly learned the Roman laws and religious customs under King Ancus himself; and he had vied with all in duty and loyalty to his prince and even with the King himself in his bounty to others.[1]

He hardly need remind the assembly of his contribution in the war of Rome against Fidene, when he made Fidene fall by digging a tunnel from the camp into the city; nor when, five years later, he compelled Veii to purchase peace by the cession of the seven Pagi near the Janiculum, which had thus become Roman territory, and by giving up the Maesian forest and the salt marshes near the mouth of the Tiber. The people of Rome were well aware that it was on his advice that Ostia was built on this spot, the first port of Rome. And equally at his suggestion were the salt works of Lacus Ostiae established. The port of Ostia was now filled with the ships of Rome and the new city of Ostia flourished greatly. Lastly, everybody knew that he had urged King Ancus in the architectural development of Rome. He had been the originator of the Fossa Quiritum that completed the defenses of the city; and he had suggested the building of the Mamertine prisons in order to preserve discipline and order. In a word, he, Lucius Tarquinius, had already ruled, under the name of Ancus, for sixteen years.

The assembly elected him King.

Thus had Rome passed from the Latins and Sabines entirely to the Etruscan dynasty of the Tarquins.

The same ambition which had prompted Tarquin the First to aspire to the crown, followed him on the throne. And being no less mindful of strengthening his own power than of increasing the power of Rome, he elected a hundred new senators, chosing them from the younger families, who, from that time, were called Minorum Gentium—a king's party, by whose favor they had entered the senate.

---

[1] Livy, I, 35.

The rulers in Tarquinia saw the immense advantage to be derived from the presence of this active Etruscan in the boundary city of Rome. They pointed out to Tarquinius the advantage to the good cause, by turning the Etruscan interest in the city of Rome into an aristocratic Tarquinian rule. They assigned to him the difficult task of counteracting the spreading influence of the popular party and converting the stronghold of Rome into the bulwark of the Tarquinian patriciate.

The rulers in Tarquinia knew only too well that the self-appointed descendant of the great Tarchun would be proud to answer the call in the name of the ancestral trust. Tarquinius Priscus' whole reign became a struggle against the liberal and democratic influence of the people of Rome. Ancus, the fourth traditional King of Rome, had been commonly regarded as the father of the plebs. And Rome now represented four different nations: Alba, Sabina, Etruria and Latium. The first three dwelt within the walls, were patrician and ruling classes, composing the senate and populus without whom the King could not act; and the fourth was an inferior adjunct, settled outside the walls, possessing certain privileges and forming an integral part of the nation, but being consulted only when the patrician tribes disagreed. The new Latins had not been convened to the Aventine, when they had become Roman plebs, for they were too numerous, and the removal of so large a population would have left the remote lands waste; but those who chose to move away were permitted to live upon the Aventine under their own laws. Most of them, however, had remained at home; but they were no longer independent and their lands were divided into three parts: one part was returned to themselves as Roman subjects and plebeian tribesmen; another was common to all the patricians of the state; and the third belonged to the crown and was in the power of the king, to use for his government or to portion away.

After the death of King Ancus, Tarquinius had set aside the compact by which the senate was bound to award the throne to one of its own members, Latin or Sabine, alternatively; and having availed himself of his great personal influence with the curiae, in which the luceres were a numerical third, he had himself elected. The curiae overawed the senate to confirm the election, and Tarquinius rewarded them by raising immediately, by royal order, one hundred luceres to become part of the senate and to take their place ever after in that body, by the side of the Ramnes and Tities.

Having thus compensated the younger families, or luceres, with one hundred seats in the senate for their support in appointing him King, he henceforth counted for the stability of his power upon the support of the luceres and became Etruria's ruling resident in Rome. Rome had become, since her early years, the theater in which was displayed the great struggle of political parties for pre-eminence in Etruria—an asylum for the fugitives and discontented of Italy, and a place where all strangers might find a home. Tarquinius himself had been one. The dominant party in Tarquinia was obliged to have a resident beyond the Tiber, to counteract the influence of the discontented and the agitations of the struggling Etruscan plebs. Now the "Etruscan resident" was the very King of Rome.

II

The first war Tarquinius waged was with the Latins from whom he took the town of Apiolae, one of the freed townships of Alba, and completely destroyed it.

The reason for the war is not clear, the most probable explanation being that the town was very rich and Tarquinius wanted money and treasure in order to start the public works he had in mind. Indeed, he celebrated the victory with games at more cost and with more magnificence than on any previous occasion; and he marked out the place for the new circus, which was forever called Maximus.

The ground for the circus, however, had to be drained before the foundations could be laid; and this prompted Tarquinius to go ahead at once with the work for the Cloaca Maxima. It was one of the greatest and most spectacular public works the history of Rome ever registered—a work that was indeed built for eternity, for it is still extant after twenty-seven centuries.

The foundations were laid forty feet underground. The branches of the main channel were carried under a great part of the city and brought into one grand trunk which ran down into the Tiber, exactly to the west of the Palatine Hill. Thus the Cloaca drained the waters of the low grounds on both sides of the Palatine, of the Velabrum between the Palatine and the Aventine, and of the site of the forum between the Palatine and the Capitoline. The stone employed in the Cloaca was not the peperino of Gabii and the Alban Hills, nor the travertino, or limestone, that was quarried in the neighborhood of Tibur, the material used later in the great works of the early emperors. It was the stone found in Rome itself, a mass of volcanic material coarsely cemented together, which afterward was supplanted by the finer quality of the peperino. It was a colossal work, which proves the greatness of the power that effected it; a work created by taskwork, like the great buildings of Egypt.

The Cloaca Maxima was built in three arched vaults, the innermost forming a circle of eighteen Roman hands in width and height. The mouth into the Tiber was the same size. All the adjoining cloacae were formed of hewn blocks of stone, tunneled out of the seven hills, seven and a quarter hands wide and four and one-sixth high. The stones were fixed without cement and the greater part of them have never required repair.[1] The arches of the branches which drained the Palatine and the Saturnian, the Quirinal and the Coelian, where the waters in winter used to run like rivers, were so high that a cart of hay could pass under them, and so wide that a navigable stream could run freely through them, and so strong as to support above them the weight of many-storied houses.[2] They were cut through the hills and masses of rock, and when they had to be repaired, the censors gave one thousand talents to the person who undertook to cleanse them.[3] The largest of all the sewers could not be finished by Tarquinius Priscus, for it took about eighty years to complete;

---

[1] When Pliny (XXXIII) examined this gigantic work seven hundred years after its construction, he gave us an account of it which exceeds all that one could have imagined of its vastness and strength.

[2] Agrippa, Prime Minister of Augustus, inspected the Cloaca Maxima and was able to traverse it from end to end in a boat.

[3] In 1742 one of these sewers was found passing under the sites of the former forum and comitium and up to the Saturnian Hill, and it was one of the few which had undergone considerable repair about the end of the First Punic War.

but he built the sections of the Velabrum, Murcian Valley and Valley of the Forum, because the Circus Maximus and the forum could not have been built, far less used, until after their construction. Tarquin the First was execrated for the cruelty and disregard of life with which he carried on this enterprise; but it was truly colossal.

The Circus Maximus was built in the Murcian Valley, for horse races and wrestling, and for religious processions and ceremonies like the circuses all over Etruria. In the case of the Circus Maximus, the pleasure which the Circensian Games gave the people made them forgive the tremendous labor employed in their creation. For the first time, special seats and stands were reserved for senators and knights and for the vestal virgins, raised twelve feet from the ground; while the general public viewed the games from many ranges of tiers. Around the circus, on the outside, there were shops under arcades, allotted to the different guilds of craftsmen, after the Etruscan fashion.

When the circus was inaugurated, Tarquinius Priscus brought horses and riders and wrestlers and all kinds of performers from Etruria. Afterward, the games continued annually, being called the Great Games. The actors who performed in the games were professional artists, hired by the impresarios who provided the games at the Aediles' orders. At times, slaves from many countries were added for their particular capacities in the art of entertaining. Actors, however, did not enjoy much respect as a class; nor were the charioteers or the gladiators held in much esteem. The only exhibitions permitted to citizens were the war dances, which were often composed of noble boys,[1] and the Atellanae, that were morality plays of a kind.

The Great Games in the Circus Maximus were held in honor of the great gods Jupiter, Juno and Minerva, and

---

[1] The tradition is mentioned by Virgil in the *Aeneis* (Canto V) and was still in use at the time of Claudius and Nero.

were celebrated each year in September, at the beginning of the sacred year. There were also games in honor of Vertumnus, Neptune, and the Penates of Rome—all Etruscan deities. The Circus Maximus was three furlongs in length and one and a half in width, and was built to accommodate 150,000 spectators!

The position of the Circus Maximus in the Murcia Valley was due to the tradition of horse racing near the underground altar of Consus, a harvest deity, and the oldest religious calendar had Equirria, or horse races, on February 27 and March 14, no doubt in connection with the preparation of the cavalry. In a very curious ancient rite known as the "October horse," there was a two-horse chariot race in the Campus Martius when the season of alms was over, and the near horse of the winning pair was sacrificed to Mars. On April 19, there was a curious practice of letting foxes run at large in the Circus Maximus with burning firebrands tied to their tails, an ancient custom which referred to the venationes, the hunts.

The Circus Maximus was built by sweated labor, but it gave the people infinite pleasure. Filled with a dense crowd, the senators in their reserved places, and the King and the magistrates presiding, it was a great sight. The chariots, usually four in number, painted either red or white, with their drivers in the same colors, issued from the carceres, or stables, at the end of the circus next to the Forum Boarium and the river, and at the signal raced around a course of 1,600 yards, divided into two halves by a spina. At the farther end of this the chariots had to turn sharply and always with a certain amount of danger, which kept the spectators in excited suspense. Seven complete laps constituted a race, and the number of races in a day varied according to the season of the year and the equipment of the particular ludi. The sympathies of the public were keenly divided between the two rival colors, the white and the red, and it is recorded that one chariot owner from Volterra in Etruria used to bring to Rome swallows daubed with his color and let them loose to fly home and so bear the news of victory!

To beautify Rome, Tarquinius erected a wall around the Septimontium and all the inhabited hills and valleys which constituted the sacred city of Rome. Only the Aventine was not walled in, for it was assigned to the plebs; nor was the Capitol, which was sacred to the patricians, nor the Janiculum, which continued to be an independent fort.

Tarquinius Priscus was interrupted in his works by the Sabine war. The hostilities were so unexpected that the enemy had passed the River Anio before the Roman army could meet and stop them. At first they fought with dubious success and there was great slaughter on both sides, which created alarm in Rome. At last, however, the Sabines were pushed back into their own camp.

Tarquinius, realizing that the weakness of his army lay in the shortage of cavalry, and determined at the same time to increase the power of his own party, made this war a pretext for creating nine hundred new knights, again to be taken from the luceres, each century of whom would have a separate vote among the populus, so as, in fact, to overpower all the other votes and throw the elections to office completely in the power of this one tribe. The old ramnes offered no resistance, for they were by then entirely crushed and nullified. But the Sabines stoutly resisted the innovation.

An ancient custom specified that one of the augurs in Rome must always be a Sabine and of the house of the Tities; and Attius Nevius, who now filled the office, a man of bold character, resolved to maintain the privileges of the Quirites. He firmly told King Tarquinius that he was going beyond his power and was infringing the sacred laws.

Not accustomed to contradiction, Tarquinius mocked the Sabine augur, and told him that with all his pretensions of being able to interpret the divine will, he could not even guess the thoughts of a mere man nor say whether or not the thing which he, the King, was at that moment meditating, was possible. The augur unhesitatingly answered that it was possible. With a laugh Tarquinius told him that he was wondering if he could cut the whetstone beside him with a razor. The augur took a razor and instantly cut the stone through.

Tarquinius bowed reverently to the minister of the gods, and said he would not increase the centuries nor oppose the divine law. He never missed an opportunity; and immediately had a statue of Attius the augur erected in the forum, with his head veiled, upon the very steps on the left of the senate house, on the spot where the supernatural deed occurred.

But Tarquinius did not abandon the plan on the success of which he felt rested the final stability of his dynasty. He distributed the nine hundred new knights amongst the old ones, making three double centuries, so that one half of all the votes were not only those of his own countrymen, but of his own creatures; and of the six half centuries, four were luceres.

Eventually Tarquinius defeated the Sabines in the war with his well-appointed cavalry; but he also had recourse to a stratagem. He had persons secretly throwing into the river Anio a great quantity of timber which they set on fire. The wood, being placed on rafts and kindled by the wind, when it stuck, firmly impacted against the piers, set the bridge on fire, striking terror into the Sabines and impeding their flight, so that many perished in the water. Their arms floated down the Tiber, and actually brought the news of the victory into the city before any account of it could be officially carried.

The new cavalry pursued the Sabines' infantry, who fled to the mountains, but the majority of them were driven by the cavalry into the river. Tarquinius decided to pursue the enemy to the bitter end, and after sending the booty and the prisoners to Rome, he proceeded with his army into the Sabine territory. A hastily raised army of the Sabines was again defeated on their own ground, and at last they sued for peace.

Collatia, a beautiful town, was taken by storm, and Tarquinius imposed on it the form of unconditional surrender that was called *deditio*. The King asked the heralds: "Are you ambassadors on the part of the people of Collatia to surrender yourselves and your city?" They answered: "We are." "Are the people of Collatia at their own disposal?" "They are." "Do you surrender yourselves and the people of Collatia, your city, lands, waters, boundaries, temples, utensils, all property both sacred and common, and do you yield them to my dominion and that of my nation?" The heralds answered: "We do surrender them." King Tarquin then said: "I do accept them," [1] and all that had once been possessed by the vanquished came to belong henceforth to the conqueror. King Tarquinius appointed his nephew Egerius, also a Tarquinian, to be lucumo of Collatia.

The Etruscan federation then admitted the Tarquinian lucumo of Rome into their own alliance, and gave him all the honors of an Etruscan king. They sent him a crown of gold, a throne of ivory, a scepter topped by an eagle, a tunic embroidered with gold and adorned with figures of palm branches, and a purple robe embroidered with flowers of various colors. These garments Tarquinius wore at his triumph; his prisoners of rank and the spoils of war followed in the procession.

He had vowed that he would dedicate part of his spoils to the Etruscan god Sethlans—Vulcan—or god of fire, to whom, since the times of Romulus, a temple had been built near the comitium. The rest of the spoils, including the revenues of the conquered territory, Tarquinius dedicated to build a temple to the great threefold Etruscan Jupiter—Jupiter, Juno and Minerva under one roof, typifying the three attributes and powers of wealth, strength and wisdom. But he had only time to choose the ground and collect the material for this great temple.

---

[1] For the form of *deditio* see Livy, I, 38, 39.

When he had been admitted into the Etruscan league and was now entitled to appear at the annual parliament of Voltumna, Tarquinius Priscus felt he had attained the summit of his ambition. He used to appear in public in a gilt chariot drawn by four horses, dressed liked a monarch of the East, in purple and gold, with the crown upon his head, the scepter in his hand, and attended by the twelve lictors with the axes and fasces.

III

Tarquinius Priscus had a sorrow, however, deep in his heart: he had no son to succeed him when his day would come. His only son had died in battle, leaving two children, Lucius and Aruns—traditional names in the princely families. Queen Tanaquil advised Tarquinius to designate his two grandchildren as his natural heirs. She herself took in hand the education of the boys.

When the proper time came she sent them to Tarquinia, to be educated foremost in the Disciplina Etrusca so as to be fit to undertake the ruling duties which one day would come their way; and Queen Tanaquil chose the chief haruspex of the capital city to be their tutor.

Soon the tutor reported that of the two boys the more alert was Aruns, the younger; he it was that showed inclination to learn and eagerness to be brought up in the tradition of the great founder.

The very landscape of Etruria had deeply affected the boy. Tarquinia was no great distance from Rome, and yet the land was quite different. It seemed to young Aruns that the landscape of Etruria was surrounded by a strange aura; that the cities were strangely hidden, some of them so well cut off, so isolated, seeming to be a mirage rather than cities.

From the mountains of Luni, in a vast arch to north and east formed by the short river Magra and the thick woods of the rocky Apennines, and then by the course of the Tiber down to the sea and on the west by the Tyrrhenian shore, the territory was hilly and mountainous, with soft undulations and here and there some isolated peaks. Broad deep valleys were formed by the Arno, the Chiana, the Tiber and the Ombrone, with rocky shores and promontories. The Apennines made a vast arch of the stone that gave the mountains a bluish color; but at the northern end one was blinded by the white quarries of Luna and Carrara. Down south, near Cecina, the mountains were metalliferous, with iron, lead, tin, and strange sprays blowing upward from the earth, white with borax. Not far from the coast, there was the Isle of Elba, with its dark rocks that the sea had cut like a knife, revealing a green texture wonderfully streaked. On the hills of Etruria the vegetation was luxuriant: the olive groves shimmered in the sun with their silvery leaves; above them rose the dark cones of the cypresses. Everywhere were woods of oak and ilex.

The landscape was both verdant and dramatic; one would have thought it was the abode of the gods, protective and intimidating, for the ravines of purple-colored tufa rock were impervious, like titanic walls. Beyond the cities and their vast necropolis, the hills merged with the encircling Apennines, a country full of dark forests, here and there glittering with olive groves; and against the paleness of the gnarled trees the long ranges of dark cypresses were like brooding giants mounting guard over the funereal hypogea. Vast forests of oaks and dark beeches filled the plains which formerly had been marshes, and the ground revealed its volcanic origin with mysterious jets of hot vapors. Not far from the site of the Cemetery of Tarquinia flowed the river Tiber, sweeping in ample curves its golden course to the sea in two branches, just below Rome.

It was a stark and inspiring scene. One heard the cry of the blue-eyed owl; in the sky flew the falcon, and there was the scent of a strange hay, rich with fragrant herbs. The men of this region had bitter faces, almost cruel; and they seemed endowed with a perceptivity and intelligence that gave them a knowledge of things and industries and sciences that were unknown to other men.

Tarquinia had greatly impressed young Aruns. The massive walls of the city, sitting upon a knoll, were truly cyclopean walls. Built of huge blocks of stone, some twelve feet long and more than six feet wide, the wall was large enough to allow two warriors in full regalia to pass each other on sentry duty. From the squat observation towers the sentries watched the valleys below the city and the limitless surface of the sea on which they could see the square, colored sails of the Etruscan fleet and of their merchant ships returning from the lands beyond the Pillars of Hercules. The Etruscan ships were much broader and higher than the vessels of Greece, which were typically slender. The Etruscan ships, which were built in the shipyards at Cosa, were heavier to maneuver, but had greater stability.

Tarquinia was no longer the town that Tarchun had built seven centuries previously. With the passing of centuries, the city had grown in size and beauty. The Cardo, or Via Principalis, running from south to north, was forty-five feet wide and it was intersected by no less than three decumanae, or broad streets, each forty-five feet wide, while the minor streets were never less than fifteen feet in width. The principal roads had two footpaths fifteen feet wide, the other fifteen feet being left for traffic. The whole city was planned on streets traversing each other at right angles, which gave the town a regular and noble appearance. Between one street and another rose blocks of high residential houses, planned as buildings rigidly rectangular, with the walls built of bricks not completely baked; the outer walls were usually faced with plaster painted in gay colors. At the side of the street ran the covered culverts of a perfected system of drains, which collected the waters from the private dwellings and brought them to a main cloaca that went to the sea.

On the ground floor of the houses, opening upon the sidewalks, there were shops grouped according to trades, thus increasing the ordered regularity of the city. And on the fringe of the city there were the villas and residences of the rich, surrounded by lovely gardens.

Temples abounded everywhere. They were always noble buildings, notable for their rich decorations, but a peculiar air of domesticity struck the visitor, for the sanctuaries were essentially the residence of the gods. And the gods, celestial, terrestrial and infernal, were numerous: Tivr—the Moon, or Selene; Thesan—the Aurora, or Eos; Usil—the Sun, or Helios, who was also called by the more ancient name of Catha. Two other deities much honored in Tarquinia were Maris, or Mars, and Nethuns, or Poseidon; and there were other divinities of Hellinic origin—Apulu, or Apollo; Artume, or Artemis; Hercle, or Heracles, this last having come from the Greek colony of Cuma on the Campanian shores of Magnagrecia. There were sanctuaries for Ani, who was also called Culsans, or Janus; and the nethergods were Velthurna and Ancharia and Satre, or Saturn.

The houses of ordinary people were of wood, the strong and beautiful woods of Etruria, hung with tiles and with outside staircases; but the better ones had loggias, and many of them also had pillared halls and colonnades.

The palace of the lucumo was on the higher part of the city. The front of the building was decorated with roof tiles in terracotta, beautifully modeled as heads of women within garlands of flowers, or as harpies, with enigmatic faces, and Gorgons' heads with headdresses of serpents, their eyes staring in hallucination and terror. The palace had a monumental gateway, from which a well-proportioned corridor gave access to a small court: on two sides of this atrium opened small sitting rooms. From them a door gave access to a vast audience room opening upon several smaller rooms. On the right there was the tablinum, or dining hall, gracefully decorated with pillars and painted walls.[1]

The furniture in the houses was usually sparse, as the Etruscans spent their days in the markets or in the forum, returning home only for meals and to sleep. Therefore the most important houses were more luxurious than comfortable. But commercial intercourse with Greece and the Near East had brought many refinements. The Asiatics provided the silk and other textiles that some centuries later had to disappear again from use and became utterly unknown till the last century B.C.; Greek art had opened to the Etruscan craftsmen and artists an unlimited field for imaginative decoration of their wares and ornaments. And the Etruscans, young, industrious and with a vision of life both realistic and without illusion, had absorbed those influences and developed them in forms seldom attained since and never surpassed in ancient times.

From the heights of Voltumna one could see the port of Tarquinia, or Graviscae as it was called,[2] which stretched inland through a covered-in watercourse roofed over with a barrel vault about thirty feet high—an amazing work, made of large blocks of stone fitted together without mortar.

This waterway was but one of the many canals that had been built to drain the marshy land and to serve as a source of life and fertility. Not much farther away, the Cosa's canal was a feat of hydraulic engineering. In the steep cliff face a huge cleft had been utilized by being widened to divert the canal through an angle of 180 degrees to continue its course underground; and as an extension of the natural cleft a tunnel was driven through the cliff, to open on to the sea about a hundred yards farther on.

Furthermore, to avert the danger of silting up and blockage, the Etruscan engineers had placed a stone barrier at an

---

[1] The plan of the house was the same as one can see at Herculanum and Pompei, the true descendants of the Etruscan tradition.
[2] Now Porto San Clementino.

angle to the opening of the tunnel to break the force of the waves, while the canal waters poured unhindered into the sea behind the shelter of it. To complete this ingenious design, they had also devised a sort of safety valve in the form of a small side tunnel branching off just in front of the main outlet. This flowed into the sea near the breakwater, creating an undercurrent which drew off any sand or seaweed that found its way into the main channel.

One day, at sunset, the boy Aruns went to visit his tutor at the temple, which was the official residence of the chief haruspex.

The chief haruspex was in his study, which, through a passage, led up to the tower for observing the sky and the stars. He was, at the moment, intensely occupied in examining the entrails of a lamb, which had been slain during the daily offering at the altar, and he still wore on his head the leather cap, that was wide at the base narrowing to a blunt peak.

When the boy was escorted into the room by an acolyte, the haruspex frowned at the disturbance; but recognizing the young prince, he beckoned him to approach.

"You might as well understand the purpose and meaning of this ritual. I am busy considering the conformation of the victim's liver at the light of the Liver of the Book."

And with the spatula which he held in his right hand he pointed to a large liver, cast in bronze, that a junior haruspex was holding upon a salver.

"As you see, the surface of this model is divided by lines into many compartments. The main line divides the convex part of the liver into two lobes, one of which is inscribed Usils, the Sun; and the other Tivr, the Moon. The Sun is the favorable part, the familiaris; while the Moon is the hostilis, the unfavorable. Then, as you see, the concave part is divided by lines along the border into sixteen compartments, which correspond to the cardinal divisions of the heavens. The inside is again divided into forty compartments, each marked

with the name of a god—Tinia, Fufluns, Turan, Turms, Te-
san, Sethlans . . .[1] Each compartment represents the seat of a
divinity, enabling the haruspex to discover on the liver of the
sacrificed animal which God is manifesting his will, and to
interpret it."

He let his eyes rest awhile upon the boy's intent face; then
he added: "The emblematic liver is the celestial residence of
the gods and also the seat of the soul. It is, in fact, the symbol
of the universe." [2]

With a slight movement of the hand the haruspex signified
to his assistant that he might retire; then he placed the spatula upon its silver stand and divested himself of the cap and
mantle. He adjusted the belt of his tunic, and taking Aruns
by the hand ascended with him to the tower. He made him
sit at his side, and for a long while they remained silent, contemplating the fading contours of the landscape and the stars
lighting up in the quickly darkening vault of the sky.

The chief haruspex liked this boy, and was happy that it
was his lot to impart knowledge to this descendant of the
great Tarchun. No one in Tarquinia had a vaster knowledge
than himself. In his youth, he had studied at the college of
Borsippa, near Babylon. Then he had visited Samothrace,
Pessinunte, Ephesus, Thessalia, Judea, the temples of the
Nabatheans, which seemed to be lost under the sands; and
from the cataracts down to the sea he had followed on foot
the whole lengthy course of the mighty Nile. With his face
veiled, he had thrown a black cock upon a fire of sandarac
before the vast bosom of the Sphinx, Mother of Terror. In
Sicily he had descended into the caverns of Vulcan and Pro-
serpine; in Lemnos he had seen the five hundred columns
of the Labyrinth turn upon themselves. He had seen the
immense candelabrum of Tarentum which had as many
branches as the days of the year. He had seen all the wonders

---

[1] Jupiter, Bacchus, Venus, Mercury, Aurora, Vulcan, etc.
[2] See Museum at Piacenza. Similar "livers," made of pottery, have been
found in Mesopotamia and elsewhere in Eastern countries. There is a relationship between the divinatory science of the Etruscans and that of the
Babylonians and Hittites.

and probed all the secrets; now, to check his own sapience and satisfy his unquenchable thirst for learning, he received, at night, some Greek visitors in order to question them.

The composition of the world troubled him no less than the true nature of the gods.

Formerly he had observed the equinox, and he had accompanied as far as Cyrene the astronomers who measured the sky by the number of their steps. Deep and wide had been his studies, so that now he no longer believed the earth to be shaped as a fir cone. He knew that the earth was round, and that it fell perpetually into the immensity, at such a prodigious speed that no one noticed the fall. From the position of the sun above the moon he had come to believe in the preeminence of Baal, whose star is but the reflected image of the god; and all he could see upon the earth brought him to admit the supreme principle of the conquering male.

Now his days were spent inspecting the censers, the golden vessels, the tweezers, the rakes for the altar ashes, and the garments of the gods and the iron that served to curl the hair and beard of Tinia on the day of the great festival. Each day, at the very same hour, he lifted the heavy tapestries from the doors of the holy cells; and there he stood with his arms wide open in the prescribed gestures; and he prayed prostrated upon the floor, while around him priests went barefooted along the corridors filled with an unending twilight.

The haruspex was loath to admit it; but he longed for a life of study and learning; and it was refreshing to impart his knowledge and his wisdom to this young prince. Aruns was only a second son; but the haruspex felt in his heart that, one day, this boy would sit on a throne.

He embraced with a wide gesture of his hands the whole firmament: "I want you, my boy, to grow up well versed in all matters of our Etruscan disciplina. Remember that the prince who, one day, may be called to be king, must be Pontifex Maximus as well as Embratur of his people. Government and religion are all one in our states. For the Etruscans the natural order of the existence of men and peoples and cities flows from the elemental powers of nature: it is the spell of a Tellurian system, where the powers of creation are also those of destruction. Life and death are one, and the existence of the whole nation, no less the existence of the individual, in all its manifestations, is part of the rhythm of this natural order. The state, with its laws and justice and civil organization, rests on a religious foundation, and any transgression of the earthly law is an offense against the divine law, a sacrilege, and it must be punished as such. The punishment, in fact, is but a propitiation to the offended god. Accordingly, everything is predestined in our world. As the Creator has apportioned to the universe a span of twelve millennia, each millennium controlled by one of the signs of the zodiac, so is the life of the individual allotted twelve ebdomades, taking as basis the fatalistic number seven: he who reaches ten ebdomades, that is, his seventieth year, can no longer postpone the incidence of fate with propitiatory rites, for he is at the mercy of his destiny; and after his eighty-fourth year his soul can be regarded as severed from his body, he is merely a living-dead, to whom even the gods pay no further attention.

"From the life of man we can pass to the life of the state—the duration of the Etruscan nation is fixed at ten cycles, or twelve centuries. Until the tenth century the menaces of Fate shall be averted and the menaces will be manifested through the centenarian prodigies, Ostenta Saecularia; but at the end of the tenth century it shall no longer be possible to deprecate the inexorable destiny. The end of each cycle is announced by the gods with appropriate signs. The first four cycles have each lasted a hundred years. When the end of our allotted time will come, the gods will let us know in their unmistakable way.[1]

"To these tenets is connected our cosmogony: [2] twelve mil-

---

1 According to Plutarch, in the year 88 B.C. the end of the eighth cycle was proclaimed by the harsh blare of a trumpet in the heaven; and Varro says that in 44 B.C. a comet announced the end of the ninth cycle.

2 There is a mention of it in the Byzantine Lexicon Suidas of the tenth century A.D. under the item "Turrenia."

lennia are fixed by the demiurge for the acts of creation; these millennia correspond to the twelve zodiacal signs. In the first millennium were created the earth and the heavens; in the second the firmament; in the third the seas and the waters upon the earth; in the fourth the great lights of heaven, the sun, the moon and the stars; in the fifth the birds, the animals and the fishes; in the sixth man was created; and the remaining millennia were assigned to the life and development of man.

"Our religion is a religion of the Book: a written religion, since the ancient times, although the dogma was transmitted orally, from Tarchun the Founder to the succeeding generations. The Books explain the cosmogony, the theology and also the Etruscan conception of time and destiny. Theory and practice are intimately connected. You will find in the Books the constant desire to penetrate and reveal the future through an analysis of the signs that the gods send to men; there are in the Books the answers to our investigating curiosity. And if you make a study of the most ancient religions, you will find that our religion is akin to, or maybe derived from, the studies of the Persian Magi.

"The Book of Lightning enumerates the various kinds of lightning and thunder, and nine are the gods who have the power of lightning, or manubia; but Tinia, the Father, has three lightnings. There are eleven different kinds of lightning. Tinia throws the first of his own will as a simple sign to take heed; the second is dangerous, and Tinia will send it only on the advice of the gods; but the third lightning, the most deadly, is issued with the concurrence of the apertanei, or the highest and mysterious gods, and it brings the destroying fire of heaven. Also Juno can issue a lightning; but Minerva possesses the Egis, the mantle bearing the Gorgon's head which is the symbol of the tempestuous forces of heaven opened out in terrible tempest. The lightning is interpreted by the Fulguriatores, who stand facing to south, so that they have eight quarters of the sky to the left and eight to the

right: flashes from the left promise good fortune, those from
the right are bad omens. And the color of lightning has its
meaning: Tinia's lightning is always blood red. If the lightning strikes a sacred spot it indicates that the gods are angry.
A man struck by lightning is looked on as favored by the
gods. And if a man of high standing is struck, that means fame
for the whole of his family. The sky is divided by the Book
into sixteen parts, based upon the cardinal points: [1] following
the point from which the lightning has started and the point
upon the ground which the lightning has hit, one deduces
which god has issued the warning. We haruspices, and in particular the Fulguriatores, can remove the traces of lightning
by burying it in the puteal, or well; and we can mitigate the
effect of the lightning or increase it against an enemy; and
equally we can attract rain in time of drought.

"Then there is the Book of Haruspices, that codifies the
science of examining the entrails of the animals slain at the
sacrifice: and the sacrifice can be of two kinds, *hostiae ani-
males* and *hostiae consultatoriae*. In the first, the victim is
offered in place of the soul or the life of the person who was
ordering the sacrifice; in the second case, the victim is killed
for the purpose of reading into its viscera the will or the advice of the god. Lastly, there is the Ritual Book, which is a
collection of all the precepts concerning the life of men and
the government of the state. Included in this Ritual Book is
the Acherontic Book, which is similar to the Egyptian Book
of the Dead, and it contains all that is necessary to know so
as to be ready for the world beyond.

"Do bear this in mind, that our religion is the result of a
subtle effort to bring to a method all superstitious beliefs and
extract from them a knowledge and a guidance. The Divine
Being is the constant father and protector of his people; his
ears are ever open to their prayers, caring for the least as
much as for the greatest, punishing equally their crimes, re-
warding their virtues, obliging them all to conduct them-

---

[1] Seneca, *Natural Questions*, 11; Pliny, *Historia Naturalis*, 11.

selves by one law. Consequently, the practice of religious ceremonies and rites can be entrusted only to a sacerdotal caste, whose members belong to the highest aristocracy—men who have, by right, a preponderance also in the political life of the state.

"Hence the supreme importance of the Pontifex Maximus and the augur whose duty is to superintend the solemnia ludorum of the sacred festivals. The augur, and with him the principal haruspices, are the arbiters of national life, as their interpretations of the victims' viscera and of thunder and lightning and of the birds' flights might decide or postpone or cancel altogether a war or a new enterprise. Our noble youths are carefully trained in the Etruscan disciplina, the mysterious science of religious divinations, that may be such a powerful weapon in political life. The haruspex who, with the corner of his mantle pulled over his head, can read the omens in the victim's liver that he is holding in his left hand, may advise the senate or the commander in war. And the augur who expounds the will of the gods and consults it according to the word of the Books, is a sacred person, whose office raises him above fear in the discharge of his duty, and he must be supported at public expense so that he might be above bribery. Without the augur there can be no election to any office—no king, no pontifex, no vestal virgins, no fecials, no priests. The augur is always a lucumo and a prince, no man of low class being eligible. And he must also have a knowledge of military matters, for no general can cross a river or a frontier, or commence a battle or divide the conquered land among his soldiers without the augur's permission."

Some time later the tutor took his pupil to visit the cemeteries.

The Necropolis of Tarquinia was connected to the city by a road more than a mile long, which started at the Decumana Gate and was called Via Inferi. This road to Avernum passed through low ranges of rocks till it reached the ceme-

teries—a vast buried city in which there were tunnels, secret
passages, mysterious corridors that the soft tufa stone made
easy to excavate, but which only an instinct for the fantastic
and the occult could have suggested.

The Necropolis showed quite clearly the stages of the Etruscan development: the more ancient tombs had the shape of
domed tumuli above the ground; the more recent ones were
recognizable by an entrance, a kind of gateway that gave access to the house below. But always the Etruscans had carved
for their dead stone mansions out of the rock, and decorated
them and furnished them as the homes of eternity. In the
older ones, the household utensils and the emblems of the
deceased's calling were graven on bas-reliefs upon the walls of
the rooms; in the later ones utensils and appurtenances, of
bronze or of gold, were deposited upon the stone couches or
suspended on the walls.

The chief haruspex slowed his step to look at the archways,
to point out to Aruns the names of the families. He always
felt awed by the figurations of death in the tombs. Sometimes
the departure from the world of the living was depicted as an
abduction of the dead by a youthful demon with winged feet
and wings on his shoulders; or the deceased was represented
upon a chariot, descending to the netherworld escorted by
one or more demons. There was a tomb in which the dead
was portrayed seated in a biga, escorted by a female demon,
an infernal Lasa who, like a Parca, held in her right hand a
roll upon which were listed the good and evil deeds of the
departed.[1] And there were journeys depicted on foot and on
horseback—the devil's horse.

The two visitors looked at the infernal beasts: the serpent,
symbol of the earth to which it clings and creeps around; the
wolf, whose skin was worn by the god of Avernum. Elsewhere
the dead was pictured descending into Hades and placating
a threatening monster surging from a puteal by pouring upon
the monster's head the contents of a patera. "This," the tutor

---

[1] Tomb dei Sette Camini near Orvieto.

said, "is a symbol of the victory of the righteous soul over the perverse forces of the subterranean world." And he smiled at the figurations of winged female demons, in girded dresses; and on one tomb was described the cruel parting of a wife from her husband and her children: but the dear lady, in a short dress falling from her shoulders, was escorted by a youth with the face of a fury: the demon had a frenzied face and disordered hair, and threateningly held a torch.

The haruspex spoke to Aruns of the theory of the souls that descend upon the earth following the same route of the sun through the signs of the zodiac. "The souls of the dead," he was saying, "dissolve in the moon like the corpses under the earth. Their tears compose the moisture of dew; and their sojourn there is dark and sad, and often full of tempest." And he added: "The miracle, the virtue of life is the light!"

He could not tell the meaning and reason of all this world of demons: perverse or benign devils, some white in the face and body, some black, some trailing the barrow upon which was seated the dead; some naked, youthful and attractive, others acting as cooks and servants in a vast scene depicting a banquet. Some carried hammers, some hatchets, which were the symbols of death and of time. One figure showed quite clearly the blow inflicted by the demon—that was the moment of change from life to death.

"Charon," murmured the haruspex; "the ferryman of the dead over the Styx," and he recalled a most beautiful tomb he had seen at Veii, on which was painted the figure of Achilles sacrificing the Trojan prisoners on the grave of Patroclus and, standing next to Achilles, an old man—Charon—with a long gown and a hat, holding the symbolic hammer. And the mentor mentioned the terrible tomb in the Necropolis of Tarquinia, in which he had seen Charon depicted with two immense wings turned upward, that seemed to vibrate to an inner wind; and upon his head Charon had two snakes twisted and tied, with the narrow heads lifted high up; and his own head had a horse's ears and a beak, a terrible and gruesome beak like a vulture. . . .

No, he would not want to be met in Avernum by such a
Charon; luckily the Achaerontic Book said that by offering
the warm blood of certain animals to some deities the soul of
the deceased would turn divine and escape the laws of death.
He wished his tomb to be an Elysium of perpetual pleasure,
with dances, games and hunting, and to have the eternal banquet depicted upon his tomb: he wished to be portrayed over
his tomb with his wife upon a bed in a flowered garden, and
a Ganymede would be near, pouring wine into the cup. And
he would be dressed in his priestly robe and mantle, and his
wife adorned with her beautiful jewels, shimmering into
death with the sun of the purest of gold.

A custodian of the Necropolis bowed to the insignia of the
illustrious visitors, and volunteered news and information:
"Had the chief haruspex and his friend seen the newest style
of decorations in the tomb of the Princess?" Preceding them
invitingly, he pushed open a gate. Out of mere curiosity, they
followed and descended into the subterranean hall. The
stone walls were covered with a layer of plaster, painted red
with cinnabar from the mines of Mount Amiata. Upon the
walls were scenes of beautiful horses with riders, the outlines
drawn in graffito and filled in with dark-brown coloring for
the horses and bright cream for the riders. The paintings
went around the walls of the three apartments composing the
vast mausoleum—a display of games, horsemanship, boxing,
a monkey, some love-making; all in honor of a lady seated
under a parasol. On the principal tomb stood the images of
the princess and her prince, their hair beautifully dressed—
somewhat Assyrian in style. The man had a pointed beard;
the woman's head was covered with the close-fitting cap of
the tutulus. Her sumptuous dress was spread out in stiff folds,
her hands outstretched in a sacrificial gesture. Both their
faces were serene, smiling. And both figures reclined upon
their left arm, which was traditional, as the figure could, in
this posture, hold in the right hand the patera with which
grain or wine was meant to be poured upon the sacrificial

altar. In the center of the patera there was a knob which, underneath, was hollow, to place inside it the forefinger to hold the cup; and on the patera was an obolus, the entrance fee to the netherworld.

Coming out of the tomb, the haruspex looked at the cheerful anteroom with its sloping ceiling and the central beam picked out with a broad line of red. On the wall between the two doorways that led to the inner chamber there was a large painting showing Achilles waiting in ambush at the spring for Troilus. It was a delightful picture, the warrior in full armor hiding behind the basin of the fountain on which two lions acted as waterspouts. Troilus was shown approaching, riding naked on a huge horse, on his feet high-pointed shoes in the archaic Etruscan fashion, and upon his head a cap with a fluttering kerchief. A landscape with a palm tree and some clusters of bushes and branches added grace to the composition, and below it ran a row of little trees hung with garlands and wreaths and ribbons, like the frame of a tapestry.

As a true Etruscan, the chief haruspex believed deeply in the destiny of the dead and in the world beyond. The Etruscan art—he explained to his pupil—in its most impressive creations was always concerned with a funeral destination. It was a complex conception: the care that was given to the construction and furnishing of the tombs showed their deep belief in a survival beyond death.

"Offerings and funeral sacrifices are meant to assure the prolongation of life beyond. The dead need the libation wine and sacrificial meat to give them new strength. No one is sure about the localization of the world beyond. Are the dead spending their destiny in the hypogea in which they are laid at rest, or are they meeting in the netherworld? Maybe the shades descend into a vast cave deep down into the bowels of the earth, into a mundus that is a high-vaulted fosse which puts into communication the world of the nether with the world of the living. Even our mirrors, reflecting upon their polished surfaces the images of the living, are indeed sym-

bolically engraved with a goddess of feminine adornment
that is called mundus: and mundus means not only the feminine adornment, but also the celestial bodies, adornment of
the heavens. On the religious days the mundus opens, and the
nether spirits return upon the earth through the terrible
fosse. You can see that this conception is illustrated in
all cemeteries: the mortuary chambers are harmoniously
adorned all along the sepulchral routes, and the corridors cut
into the rock go deep down into the earth, adducting to the
houses of the dead which are but replicas of the houses of the
living."

They reached, at last, the tomb of Tarchun. The mausoleum of the great Founder was a lofty tumulus of the archaic
type and was now a sanctuary where offerings were made and
auguries taken.

The priest in attendance bowed to the chief haruspex and
to the young descendant of the Founder, touching his white
pointed miter with the tip of the spatula he carried in his
right hand. Then he removed a few stones from the upper
part of the door. Through an aperture the visitors saw, lying
in state upon the stone couch, the image of the Founder.
They saw him outstretched upon the stone bed, a stone pil-
low for a headrest, crowned with the double crown of king
and augur, all clothed in armor; his shield, his spear and his
arrows were by his side. And on the middle finger of his right
hand he wore the sacred scarabaeus, engraved with the images
of the Egyptian gods.

But the ashes of Tarchun were in the canopic vase that
rested upon the sella or curule chair: a strange bronze vase of
almost human form. The lid was like a man's head, virile of
feature, adorned with two golden earrings. Was this the true
image of the Founder? Now, since a long time, the dead were
no longer cremated upon a pyre, but deposited inside the
aerated sarcophagi of beautifully decorated terracotta, and
the images resting upon the lids were the true representations
of the dead, often ordered in advance by the living them-

selves. But who could say what the great Tarchun had really looked like? The image that stood in the tomb was imaginary, like the statue of a god. But whose face was the head that made the lid of the original canopus?

So they stood contemplating the features of the head that closed the canopic vase containing the ashes. "I like," said the mentor, "I like to think that they are the Founder's true features—so strong, so noble, so determined!" And he recalled the pomp that had honored his funeral, the people of Tarquinia all attending it, the senators, the vestal virgins and the rich and the honorable, all assembled to watch the Palestric Games, the boxing and wrestling and the racing which were performed for the great departed, while the crowd joined in the loud and mournful lamentations for his loss. These games had their origin in Egypt, and were depicted in the Egyptian tombs, many centuries before the Rasenna had come from the delta to colonize Etruria. In the manner of Egypt, the deeds of Tarchun had been rehearsed at his interment and his praise sung; and the funeral song said that he was worthy of converse with the Genius of Etruria, for he had passed to the Rasenna the laws and institutions of Tages.

Reverently the chief haruspex touched the spatula of the priest with his fore and middle fingers and brought them to his forehead in the ritual way. Rather awkwardly the boy did the same. Then they turned from the door and sat for a while at the foot of the smiling Sphinx that guarded the entrance.

"Yes," the haruspex was saying, "the cemeteries are the serene cities of the dead; cities that are not only invisible, but the whole world is made invisible to their inhabitants. There is no horizon to gaze at, almost no sky above the Necropolis, so determinedly have the Etruscans burrowed into the ground. But at Tarquinia the tombs are built on the highest hills with the widest horizon. Look! From the tumulus of Tarchun we can see the mountains encircling Rome; and a long stretch of the coast is visible. Into these tombs, all the wealth that has been accumulated, all the glory hallowed in paintings, statues and busts and portraits, all the finest vessels and utensils, all the most valuable and beautiful things have been laid for the enrichment of the dead! These tombs are the eternal witness of the Etruscan glory. By these tombs let us commune with the spirit of your great ancestor."

IV

While the two young princes were being educated at Tarquinia, a strange event happened in the palace in Rome. It was a most singular prodigy: the head of a boy, Servius Mastarna, son of an Etruscan chief, and familiarly called Tullius, was seen to blaze with fire while he lay fast asleep.

The noise of those present at so miraculous a portent roused from their beds the King and Queen; and Queen Tanaquil prevented a servant from extinguishing the flames till the boy should awake. As soon as he opened his eyes the flames disappeared.

Queen Tanaquil called Tarquinius in private, and said to him: "This boy that we have been bringing up in so mean a style will be a light to us in our adversity and a protector to our palace in distress. Let us bring up this youth in a royal manner."

She sat with her husband on the couch drawn up near the double bed, as high as an altar, upon which rested two conical hats surrounded by crowns, each placed on the pillows; and she and her husband poured a libation over the bed. Old King Tarquinius hesitated as to what part he should act toward the boy; but Queen Tanaquil advised him to propitiate him and, in due course, bind him to them by marriage. From

that day she supervised his education, and brought him up to
be worthy of the highest office.

The young man turned out to be of a truly royal disposi-
tion; and thus it came to pass that when Tarquinius had
reigned thirty-eight years, Servius Tullius was in the highest
esteem, not only with the King but also with the senate and
people.

At this time the two sons of the late King Ancus Marcius,
who had always considered it an indignity that they should
have been deprived of their father's crown by their guardian
Tarquinius, who was a stranger and not even of a Roman
family, felt their indignation rise to a still higher pitch at the
notion that the crown of Romulus would not only not revert
to them but pass to a man whose very name, Servius, classified
him as a slave.

They arranged a plot to kill the old King. Two villainous
shepherds were selected for the deed, and they were to accomplish it with their rustic implements, by conducting
themselves in a violent manner in the palace porch so as to
draw the attention of the King's attendants. Then, they would
both appeal to the King. So it happened, and amidst great
clamor the two shepherds were brought into his presence and
the King commanded them to speak in turn. While one began to state the reason for their quarrel, the other suddenly
raised his ax and struck it into the King's head, leaving the
weapon in the wound.

An uproar followed; but Queen Tanaquil ordered the
palace to be closed and turned out all who were present: and
sending immediately for Servius, she showed him the King
in his last moments. Holding Servius' right hand, Queen
Tanaquil entreated him not to allow the death of his father-
in-law to go unavenged, nor his mother-in-law to be an object of insult. "Servius," she said, "if you are a man, the
kingdom is yours, not theirs who, by this plot, have perpe-
trated the crime. Follow the guidance of the gods, who portended that your head would be illustrious by shedding a
blaze around it!"

Outside the palace, the people were in confusion. Queen Tanaquil addressed the populace from a window on the upper floor; she bade the people to be of good heart; told them that the King was only stunned by the blow and was already coming to himself again, and she commanded them, in the meantime, to obey the orders of Servius Tullius, who would perform all the functions of the King.

At Tanaquil's bidding Servius showed himself with the trabea and the lictors, dressed in the toga woven for him by Queen Tanaquil; and he seated himself on the throne. When several days later the King's death was announced, Servius, supported by a strong guard, took possession of the kingdom by consent of the senate, and assumed the name of Servius Tullius. Ancus' sons had already sought safety in flight, and went into exile at Suessa Pometia.

Queen Tanaquil's policy in foisting her protégé Servius Mastarna on the throne was quite logical and well-calculated —rather than let the kingdom revert to Ancus' family, it was better to preserve it in Etruscan hands and trust to chance for the succession of her nephews who were, in any case, much too young to be as yet considered. At the worst, Servius Tullius was bound by marriage to the Tarquinian dynasty.

It proved a sound calculation, for Servius Tullius was a wise and shrewd man, and when the proper time came, lest the feelings of the grandchildren of Tarquinius Priscus might be the same toward himself as those of the sons of Ancus had been toward the dead King, he gave his two daughters in marriage to the young princes, Lucius and Aruns Tarquinii.

Servius was thirty years old when he ascended the throne; and he found himself King of Rome and Ardea, Antium, Circei and Terracina, and of the lands of the Rutuli and Volsci. By Tarquin the First, Rome had been introduced into the maritime and commercial world, and Aricia and Laurentum had already sent their ships to sail in company with the justice-loving Cerites and the enterprising Populonians. The amity and protection of Etruria had given Rome the means and capacity to rule.

But King Servius thought it safer for his throne to give rein to the independence of the plebs. No one was further than the former Mastarna from any idea of equality of men, or the leveling of classes, for he descended from an Etruscan house and had been brought up by Queen Tanaquil; yet one of his first acts was to create at first six, and then twelve new bodies of knights, with hereditary rank, to head all the plebeian assemblies.

He allowed these new knights to live upon the Coelian, ordering the patricians to quit that hill, and to placate their feelings he allotted to them new residences in the valley, which became known as Vicus Patricius. At the same time, however, he forbade all the patricians in the city to fortify their houses, as they had been in the habit of doing.

Servius' main object was to build a political and military power which would be antipatrician. Not to oppose what common custom had made men regard as the irrevocable order of creation, he did not attempt to wrest from the patricians the offices of state, nor did he tax them or impose upon them new duties. He left to the patricians all their clients and the power which they had of relieving any plebeian from distress, by receiving him into their clans.

But he ordained that henceforth all the Roman infantry employed and paid by the state should be plebeian, and only plebeian.[1]

This was the great reform of Servius Tullius. He divided the whole population of Rome into thirty plebeian tribes, answering to the thirty patrician curiae. He divided them by the sacred Etruscan numbers, three and ten, allotting ten to the Ramnes, ten to the Sabines and ten to the Etruscans, or Tuscans as they were now called in Rome. A division of the people into tribes had been made already by Tarquin the

_____
[1] Dionysius IV, 10, 13.

First, for the plebeians were taxed and voted according to their tribes, and the army was selected in the order of the tribes. What was new in Servius' reform was the equalizing of the three nations of Latins, Sabines and Tuscans in political power, allotting ten to each nation and appointing in each tribe three civil judges.

To accomplish this, Servius took a census of all the people according to their taxable property. He ordered all the citizens to give in writing their names and ages, the names and ages of their wives and children, and all the chiefs were to render an estimate of their personal property. It was the first census.

He next divided the plebeians into six classes: the first was composed of those who were possessors of 100,000 *asses* and upward; and from this there was a gradual diminution to the fifth class, which was rated at 12,500 *asses,* this being the minimum wealth entitling a man to vote. The sixth class included all those beneath this value, and these were not allowed to offer themselves as soldiers.

This census accounted for 84,700 fighting men. The census completed—and Servius had expedited it by the terror of a law passed on those not rated, with threats of imprisonment and death—he called all citizens in the Campus Martius, each in his century. There he drew up his army and performed the sacrifice called suovetaurilia, that was the closing of the lustrum, or the conclusion of the census.

To accommodate the whole population the city was enlarged, taking in two more hills, the Quirinal and the Viminal. King Servius also enlarged the Esquiline and took up his residence there, in order that respectability might be attached to the new districts. He surrounded the city with a rampart, a moat and a new wall: it was called the Servians Walls.

Not satisfied with the control that these measures gave him of the number and wealth of his subjects, Servius commanded that every citizen, upon the birth of a child, should pay a tribute in the temple of Lucina, and upon the death of a rela-

1. Head of Jupiter Capitolinus, from the temple commenced by Tarquin the First and completed by Tarquin the Proud. (*Museum of Villa Giulia, Rome*)

2. The famous group of the wolf suckling Romulus and Remus, which was outside the Temple of Jupiter Capitolinus, and became, and still is, the coat-of-arms of Rome. (*Museum of Conservatori, Rome*)

3. The Necropolis of Caere (Cerveteri), showing the archaic type of tombs above the ground known as tumuli.

4. Interior of a tomb at Caere, with domestic utensils carved in relief on the pillar faces.

5. The City of the Dead at Caere. In the foreground is the old Etruscan Via Inferi, the Road to the Underworld, with its deep chariot ruts.

The only existing, and imaginary, portrait of Lucrece, painted by Parmigiano. (*Capodimonte Museum, Naples*)

7. The terracotta Winged Horses similar to those that adorned the metope of the Temple of Jupiter Capitolinus, cast at Veii, fourth century B.C. (*Tarquinia Museum*)

8. Specimen of Etruscan writing in the Perugia Museum: the letters are clearly visible. However, the archaic Greek alphabet is written from right to left.

Tablet in lead, from Magliano, showing the inscription on a "liver" used by the haruspices in their divination.

(*Etruscan Museum, Florence*)

10. The front wall of the Tomb of the Bulls, with its striking paintings and frieze. Sixth century B.C. (*Necropolis of Tarquinia*)

11. Tomb of the Augurs, with painting of wrestlers. Sixth century B.C. (*Necropolis of Tarquinia*)

tive a tribute should be paid in the temple of Juno Libitina or Inferna, and on reaching manhood a tribute in the temple of the Sabine Juventus. Again, each citizen, man, woman or child, was required to pay a tax upon attending the Paganalia. In consequence the treasury became enormously rich.

The small currency used in Rome by the plebs at the time was made of leather, shells and bronze. Servius introduced the *as* grave, that was the stamped *as* of the Etruscans, with the heads of Janus or Talna, Minerva, Hercules, Mercury or Turms, and on the obverse side of all the currency appeared the Etruscan prow. An *as* weighed twelve ounces.

Every plebeian soldier was required to equip himself, and soldiers of the first class were ordered to wear rich Etruscan armor of bronze. The first class was always headed by the eighteen centuries of the plebeian hereditary knights.

The second class had carpenters, armorers and smiths attached to them, a kind of military engineers' units; and the fourth had a band of wind instruments, horns and trumpets, of which the Etruscans were the inventors. The five classes were divided into one hundred and seventy taxable centuries, of which the first class alone comprised eighty centuries, and the three first, one hundred and twenty. Therefore, if they were in agreement, the votes of the others would be of no consequence, and their decision could not be reversed because all classes were called to vote in order.

It was, quite clearly, a negation of the plebeian vote, for if the whole first class, including the eighteen centuries of knights, were of one mind, their decision was final, as their votes outnumbered all the others put together. The lower classes were scarcely ever called upon to vote. Thus the largest property carried the most votes, and the greatest number of men by far the fewest.

The centuries, excluding the hereditary knights, were again divided into equal numbers of major and minor, all the men above forty-five years of age enrolling in the one, and from eighteen to forty-five in the other. The soldiers of the major centuries were a reserve militia, who stayed at home to guard the towns and country, while those chosen from the minor were to march wherever they were required. These classes made up the great and formidable body of the Roman plebs—a grouping of men adopted from Etruria.

Nor was the order of battle and armor of Servius' army different from the Etruscan. The velites, or light troops, were similar to those of the neighboring falisci; and the galea, or helmet; the clypeus, or shield; the scaled coat of mail, the greaves; the scutum, or buckler; and the hasta, or spear, had all been copied from the Etruscans.

The four tribes of the city were divided into compitalia, with a temple situated where four ways met; and in these temples the priests were slaves.

But Servius raised the freed captives, or liberti, to the position of plebeian citizens, and enrolled them in the four city tribes, granting them the privilege of entering the army. He forbade the patricians to seize the persons of their debtors, which was a great blow to their power; and the plebs were to take charge of their own affairs, meeting in centuries in the Campus Martius, and no law passed by the senate and approved by the curiae was to be binding without their consent.

To give impulse to this, and to court popularity, he required the plebs to confirm his own election to the throne which he had wrung from an overawed senate, and upon their compliance he declared himself a duly elected King, governing with the plebs' support. Then, Servius ordered that this new constitution should be commemorated every lustrum, when the people would assemble in the Campus Martius, and not within the augury ground of the patricians. Here the centuries were drawn up in order of battle, and the solemn Etruscan sacrifice of the suovetaurilia, of a bull, a sheep and a pig, was offered for them.

Finally, having assigned the Esquiline to the plebeians Servius took the title of King of the Plebs.

He had thus given the plebs their own tribunes, judges priests, feasts, laws and property, and his last outrage upor the traditions of the ancient ruling classes was his intentior to secure for the plebs a joint or alternate possession of the crown.

This was his downfall. The patricians, already disgusted when Servius had overridden their privilege to possess all the common land—which was the fruit of the wars and victories of Tarquin the First—and divided it among the plebs, decided to get rid of this King who lived only to degrade them.

V

When the boys Lucius and Aruns returned to Rome, Queen Tanaquil was long since dead, and Servius had been King many years. The young princes thought it better to accept the situation and await events.

In due course they married the two daughters of King Servius, strangely enough both called Tullia. Aruns, the cadet, had married the meek Tullia, while the fiery one had been the lot of his elder brother Lucius.

Soon the haughty Tullia confided to her brother-in-law that she was chagrined, for there was no spirit in her husband, either ambition or bold daring. Soon she opened out her heart to Aruns: "She admired him; him she could truly call a man, and one truly descended of royal blood! And she could be to him a second Queen Tanaquil!"

The Etruscan women were not ciphers: the Tarquinian dynasty was nobly founded by Tanaquil; it could be continued by the determination of the reckless Tullia.

Soon the palace was filled with tragic guilt; ghosts walked by night; incest and tragedies were the happenings behind the throne. Two more deaths followed rapidly; Aruns Tarquin and the fiery Tullia found their houses vacant for new nuptials.

Then the aging Servius Tullius began to be every day more

disquieted, his reign more unhappy. Tullia did not let her second husband rest by night or by day, lest their murders might bring no fruit. "What I wanted," she said to Aruns, "was not a person whose wife I might be called, or one with whom I might in silence live a slave; what I wanted was one who would consider himself worthy of the throne: who would remember that he was the grandson of Tarquinius Priscus; who would rather possess a kingdom than hope for it! If you, to whom I consider myself married, are such a man, I address you both as husband and King; but if you are not, our condition has been changed for the worse, for in your person crime is associated with meanness. Why not prepare yourself? It is not necessary for you, as for your great grandfather, coming here from Tarquinia, to strive for a foreign throne. Your household and country's gods, the image of your grandfather, and the royal palace, and the royal throne in this palace, constitute and call you King! Or if you have too little spirit for this, why do you disappoint the nation? Why do you suffer yourself to be looked upon as a prince? Get back to Tarquinia; sink back again to your beginning, more like your meek brother than your great grandfather!" [1]

Can a man resist such words? Pride, vanity, ambition and lust, all the strongest instincts of man combine to make the blood beat stronger and faster within the troubled breast of Aruns Tarquin. History and the world are but a stage for the tragedies to which poets and dramatists will give words afresh that will leave men doubtful of their ever having escaped human lips.

When sure of the patricians' support, Tarquin went in the forum with a body of his own troops and laid before the senate the iniquity of tolerating a government which so peculiarly oppressed the senate and the ancient classes. He accused Servius Tullius of being himself a plebeian and the sovereign and patron of plebeians, unfit to rule the senators and the curiae.

---

[1] For this speech, that reads like lines in an Elizabethan tragedy, see Livy, *Ab Urbe Condita* I, 47.

He then seated himself in the King's place, and upon Servius' entrance in the senate, a combat ensued, which ended
with the old King being thrown down the steps of the senate
house, mortally wounded. Shortly afterward King Servius
died. His servants carried off the body, and on their way to
his palace on the Esquiline they laid it down in the Vicus
Cyprius, or Good Street.[1]

The fiery Tullia had driven to the senate to salute her husband as King; and she was on her way back to her own house
when she came to this street, and her charioteer, on seeing
the body, stopped in pity and respect. But Tullia ordered the
charioteer to drive on, over the body of the murdered Servius; and on arriving at her house she went to her domestic
altar to return thanks to her household gods. Later on, however, Tullia visited the Temple of Fortune, which had been
built by the late King; and seeing the votive image of Servius
made of gilt wood, she covered her face and went away. The
name of the street where she would not stop was henceforth
changed from Cyprius to Sceleratus.

Servius was given the funeral of an Etruscan prince. When
consulted about it, the second Tarquin scornfully answered
that Servius might dispense with a funeral as Romulus had
done before him. The delegation looked at him in surprise,
and said that it sounded like the opinion of Tarquinius Su-
perbus, Tarquin the Proud.

The surname stuck. Tarquin the Second was proud of it.

---

[1] About the year 208 of Rome.

BOOK THREE

THE
FANUM
AT
VOLTUMNA

I

There was in Etruria, in the lucumony of Tarquinia, an irradiation of valleys which formed the great national cemetery of the Etruscan nation. Indeed, it was the cemetery of the kings and heroes, like the Valley of the Kings at Thebes in Egypt.

The cemetery of the kings and heroes was now more than seven centuries old, having been founded in the thirteenth century B.C., five centuries before the foundation of Rome. The tombs had originally belonged to the warriors who had created, extended, and defended the Etruscan nation.

Not far from the cemetery of kings and heroes rose the ancient temple dedicated to the goddess of national union and concord—the Fanum of Voltumna, erected in memory of Tarchun the Founder. It was, this ancient temple, the Baal Temunch, as in some Mediterranean dialects it was called; but the Etruscans called it, in their writing, F.L.T.M.N., omitting the vocals, in the manner that was also used by the people of Carthage.

Every year on the twenty-first of April, which was the holy anniversary of the foundation of Tarquinia, the lars of the twelve Etruscan lucumonies assembled at the Fanum of Voltumna, to celebrate the birthday of the fatherland and to hold their parliament.

The annual meeting at Voltumna was both a national diet and a popular fair, and for the fair of the twenty-first of April a great number of people always came to Voltumna, merchants from distant shores, even from Asia and Africa. Big tents were erected to house the visitors; and although Voltumna was not a town, all around the fanum had grown up many hostelries and taverns.

The temple stood in the vicinity of the Lake of Bolsena. It was built of square blocks of stone, with four square pillars in front supporting an entablature and triglyph ornaments, a Doric frieze consisting of a tablet with three parallel vertical channels or glyphs, standing on each side of the metopes. Over this stood a pediment in the usual form of the Greek metope, filled with statuary.[1]

It was a large quadrangular building, some 200 feet long by 185 feet broad, and in comparison to the Hellenic temples it looked almost square. Along the face ran a portico with tall columns. Inside it had a nave and two aisles. The nave was divided into two equal parts lengthways, the inner one containing the three cells of the gods, standing side by side; and in the center were folding doors which could be opened into the sanctuary. In front of this tabernacle rose two orders of four columns, placed at such distance as to make the temple look so well balanced and aerial, that this style was called aerostili.[2] Inside the inner cell was the statue of Tinia-Jupiter, flanked by Uni-Juno and Minerva, the Celestial Triad who commanded the Lightning and Thunder. The statue of Tinia was, like all Etruscan statuary, of terracotta, with a severe expression, the face framed by regular curls, the eyes almond-shaped like the eyes of the Etruscans, the nose straight but inclined slightly downward, the mustaches following the curve of the chin, thus giving a greater kindness to the mouth, whose lips seemed in the act of uttering the

---

[1] Livy, II, 44; V, 17; VI, 2; X, 16—Dionysius, III, 61—Diodorus, V, 40.

[2] Vitruvius III—A temple dedicated to the Trinity of Avernus—Ceres, Libero and Libera—was reconstructed in Rome under Augustus in the same form in which it had originally been built by the Etruscans.

blessing of the god who was father of his people. The small, well-pointed beard added a touch of good humor to the god's countenance.[1]

The twelve lars had assembled in the early hours of the morning, each arriving at the temple preceded and escorted by twelve lictors with the fasces and rods that symbolized the league of the twelve lucumonies, individually weak but strong and unbreakable as a bundle: the fasces were topped by the double ax.

This year there were present the lars of Tarquinia, Volterra, Clusium, Cortona, Perusia, Arretium, Falerii, Volsinii, Rusella, Vetulonia, Caere and Veii;[2] the representatives from the cities and colonies in the north and south: Luna, Pisa, Fiesole, Cosa, Vulci, Agylla, Pyrgi,[3] and the deputies from the allies of Etruria: King Tarquin of Rome had been invited to attend as an ally and as a descendant of the Tarquinian House.

The first duty of the assembly was to approve the appointment of the new Pontifex Maximus, and to this purpose the meeting was attended also by the augurs, the haruspices and the feciales.

The augur of Tarquinia gave permission for the assembly to take the auspices before proceeding to the election of their president; and the chief haruspex was duly called. He moved to the center of the nave, and washed his hands in a large round lebete, a shallow bronze basin adorned around the edge with seven slender figurines playing a sacred dance.[4] A strong perfume of aromatic herbs filled the nave. The chief haruspex advanced to the sacrificial altar upon which stood a bronze lamp with sixteen branches—a most beautiful oil

---

[1] One can see the temple of the Etruscan Jupiter Capitolinus on the obverse side of some coins of Vespasian and Domitian.

[2] For their names see Dionysius, Livy, Virgil, Servius, Strabo and Plutarch.

[3] The original Etruscan names commenced, in many cases, with "Fel," such as Fel-atri—Volterra; Fetluna—Vetulonia; fel or vel meaning lord, to which syllables were added.

[4] Now in the museum at Chiusi.

lamp, shaped like a flower, from the center of which rose a glaring Gorgon surrounded by motifs in concentric circles. The cavities holding the wick were decorated alternately with sileni playing music, and harpies.[1]

The victim was slain, and the haruspex proceeded to examine the entrails. He slit the animal; two acolytes extracted the liver, each movement of their bronze tools following the ritual. The liver was deposited upon a slab of basalt while the haruspex placed himself facing south, and, holding the liver in his left hand, lifted his face to the heavens. A diseased liver indicated misfortune; an exceptionally large one foretold good fortune. The augur, dressed in white with a golden band around his head, watched the sacred rite.

The omens were good. The augur intimated that the assembly could proceed to elect the new embratur, the commander in chief under whose sole command the twelve lucumonies would march forth in case of war.

After the election, the augur made the new embratur sit on the sella curulis, the curule chair of office; invested him with the toga edged with embroidered palms; put around his neck the bulla aurea, placed on his head a golden crown of oak leaves, and a scepter in his hand. The lictors ranged themselves on the right and left of the throne.

Then the assembly discussed the order of the day. All decisions taken in the temple of Voltumna were absolutely binding for the Etruscan confederation; anyone who would dare to fail to keep them was automatically ostracized. However, on questions other than peace and war, the federal principles allowed each lucumony a wider freedom of decision, and the conclusion of pacts with non-Etruscan cities was left more or less to the discretion of each individual lar.

At sunset the lar of Tarquinia was entertaining the other lucumons at a banquet in his palace; and after the meeting all the lars and other distinguished visitors mounted their

---

[1] This lamp, of this very fifth century B.C., is in the museum at Cortona.

chariots to proceed with their followers to the capital city.

There were already many guests waiting at the palace; and the lar had planned a novelty: a wine-tasting ceremony to precede the feast. He was proud of his vineyards, where several kinds of vines were grown, and he wanted his illustrious guests to taste the various vintages of his quite famous cellar.

When the guests descended into the main cellar a cry of wonder escaped their lips: the cellar was a spacious hall, with a ceiling gaily painted with scenes from Dionysus' life, and the walls were hung with rich tapestries.

On a long table stood great bowls of wine, both golden and red, which the slaves, dressed in white tunics edged with crimson, poured from tall amphorae arrayed along the main wall in wrought-iron stands. The guests sat at three long tables on painted stools and tasted the wine, sipping it from small shallow bowls of silver with finely worked handles.

The game consisted in guessing the kind of wine and possibly the vintage. After a few sips, bowls and cups were emptied into a basin; the slaves wiped the vessels clean with a napkin and refilled them with fresh wine.

A guest said emphatically that the wine of Etruria was a definite improvement on the wine of Egypt. Everybody concurred: "It was lighter, and it had a bouquet that the Egyptian wines did not have." "Anyway," said another, "the Egyptians fabricated their story that the vineyards of Bubaste produced bunches of grapes so big that it took two men to carry them to the presses!"

When the party adjourned for dinner, the guests were in a more convivial mood. Between one sampling and another they had rinsed their mouths with olives bottled in salty and spicy water to keep them fresh, or with black, toasted olives in the Greek taste. Their tongues clicked in anticipation of the good food to come. The ladies were already in the banqueting hall on the couches, slipping off their sandals and proffering their feet to the slaves, who wiped them with perfumed water. The lucumons and all the guests walked into the dining hall, the floor of which was strewn with fine sand and rushes.

The tablinum of the lar of Tarquinia was a magnificent hall. High couches were arranged along the dining tables. Beds and tables were exquisitely worked, inlaid with plaques of embossed gold and carved ivory. Rich coverlets draped the couches, and the banqueters rested upon embroidered cushions. The tables were small, either square or oblong, with marble tops, upon which the servants placed the vessels and cups. A special richness was displayed in the great bronze tripods and the variety of gleaming candelabra, of bronze or silver. Many had lions' claws, and the shaft was topped by a god or warrior; sometimes the entire lamp represented a mythological episode. Light was provided by small torches or wicks fixed to the radiating arms; while in the tripods burned incense and perfumed oils from Carthage and Arabia. The lar's house could display that year a great novelty: a huge chandelier in the shape of a bronze bowl richly decorated, which was suspended from the ceiling. On a shelf running along a wall were displayed delightful bronze figurines, exquisitely modeled as warriors wearing the immense helmets of the heroes of Troy that were also depicted upon the Grecian vases.

On the tables, the vessels were rich and ornate, and mainly of gold. Slaves and attendants carried the dishes upon servers and in basins of embossed silver; the wines were poured from beakers sometimes having three necks, so that the guests had at once a choice of three different wines. Some beakers were of the black pottery called bucchero, finely painted in the Greek style; others had spouts shaped like trefoil; and there were craters into which one could mix several wines and spices. The lar himself was rather proud of his libation cup, in ivory of the rhyton type; and upon his table stood a small ivory statuette of the goddess of fecundity, with her hands upon her breasts and a flowing mantle of gold draped around her shoulders.

The banquet commenced with the typical Etruscan dish: boiled eggs stuffed with olives or with morsels of fish and pepper. Then came fish of many kinds, fried and grilled or in soup; crab and shellfish treated with silphium, a rare sauce prepared with a plant imported from Carthage. Then followed roast meats, venison, birds, ducks and geese, Numidian hens, peacocks and pheasants, suckling pigs stuffed with meats and aromatic herbs. The wines were local, excellent and not too powerful, and with the dessert the slaves served wines sweetened with honey. The dessert formed the second part of the banquet, and consisted of fruit, fresh and candied, and many varieties of sweets and tarts, some made with sweet cheese and eggs and honey.

King Tarquin always enjoyed a visit to Tarquinia. He felt that life was so much more advanced, cultured and refined than in Rome. Indeed, to the friends on his couch who inquired how things were going in Rome, he replied noncommittally with an airy gesture of his left hand.

A banquet was the favorite entertainment for Etruscan society, with good food, choice wines and lively conversation; and more than anything Tarquin loved the Etruscan habit of having ladies at dinner and sharing the couches with them. He knew that this custom was strongly deprecated in Rome, and in Greece too, as it was considered a sign of immorality. Some people in Rome even murmured that ladies in Tarquinia did not object to lying on the dining couches undressed and lending themselves to occasional pleasures with the guests. In Etruria one never knew whose child was whose! [1]

He glanced round the room and smiled cynically. Alas, it was as good as true, on some couches the guests did not care that people saw them while they were enjoying themselves in more than one sense! Several guests were changing couches, making a ribald jest in the process; the slaves were busy arranging around the couches screens of bamboo and rush.[1]

---

[1] Theopompus.

Somebody said to Tarquin: "It may be loose, this custom of ours, but I think it improves the race. Look indeed at our youth! We are a beautiful race." And the gentleman slapped his thigh with pride, a long, well-shaped and muscular thigh, carefully depilated like his entire body. And he added: "I have an excellent barber and depilator. He does me all over, twice a week, in some two hours, and it is quite painless."

Yes, King Tarquin thought, it was a pleasant party. He looked at the beautiful and elegant company. Before reclining upon the couches, the men had discarded the tebennos that was the symbol of command and class superiority, the mantle that in Rome had been transformed into the toga; and they now wore only a brief tunic of red linen with short sleeves, bordered at the square-cut neck and at the sleeves and hem in blue. Those who had not discarded their shoes wore open sandals of dyed leather. The vogue in hair styles for men favored the hair swept back and widened out behind the ears: a colored ribbon or a band of gold was worn to keep it in place.

The ladies were most elegantly turned out. Indeed, no one could deny that they were beautiful creatures, full of charm. In olden times their Eastern ancestry had been more marked upon their features; now they were perhaps less haughty and spirited, but their faces had a refined and spiritual beauty, with their fascinating almond-shaped eyes; and they had the aristocratic and slightly bored air of high breeding and ancient lineage.

Some wore their long hair loose over their shoulders, with a tuft of soft curls in front; others had two tresses at the side of the face and the mass done up at the back in a broad chignon. But the majority wore their hair curled and carefully swept back from the brow and arranged in a graceful knot at the back, in a style copied from Oriental fashions. Very pleasing were their gowns and dresses. The ladies no longer wore the ancient costume, long and close-fitting, with a belt at the waist and a mantle reaching to the knees and often arranged in folds. Now their dress was no different from the chiton and himation worn by Greek ladies, that emphasized the contours. There was a liking for geometrical designs in the trim of the garments; even the whole outline of the dress was markedly geometrical, almost like a trapeze, hanging from the shoulders in angular lines. The fabrics were of soft silks, or fine colored linen, printed with polka dots or sprinkled with a pattern stamped here and there and around the hem of the tunic and cloak.[1] Some dresses were very tight-fitting and accentuated the rounded lines, though suggesting a pleasant sense of movement. Others had a distinct Eastern character with a jacket that was almost a bolero. Several elderly ladies wore the tutulus, a pointing coif covering the back of the head, a traditional headdress worn by all the ladies of high station.

And what a gay variety of footwear! The Etruscans were so skilled in leather work that they were famed throughout the countries of the Mediterranean. Many of the women at the party displayed the same style of footwear, long, close-fitting boots slightly upturned at the toes, with many types of lacing. Others wore tiny moccasins made of dyed or gilt kid. One lady had blue high boots, and another wore openwork sandals, held by a tiny strap across the instep.

One lady's coiffure came undone. A female slave dresser ran at once to the couch with comb and hairpins and a large mirror; it was a very beautiful mirror; afterward it was passed around. On the chased back the mirror had a curious scene depicting Hercules with a full beard, sucking at Juno's ample breast in the presence of several other gods.[2]

Yes, the Etruscan ladies were experts at their dressing tables. The many articles and accessories were a charming proof of the care they devoted to their face and body: flasks of ivory and alabaster or of glass inlaid with gold, called aryballos, contained oils and perfumes. There were boxes for rouge; little spoons to take the make-up from the jars; instruments for the fingernails and all the paraphernalia of beauty

---

[1] See the figure of the "Offering" of the year 550 B.C.
[2] In the Archaeological Museum at Florence.

treatment. They loved to have beautiful things about their rooms: craftsmen and jewelers designed a thousand pretty things and objects of adornment and decoration for the ladies. Their round hand mirrors with long handles were works of art, of polished bronze, with the back exquisitely chased and engraved with mythological scenes or, at times, daring subjects. The best mirrors came from Vulci and Palestrina.

They had jewel boxes, caskets of bronze and silver, some decorated with pictorial engravings and charming figures on their lids for handles, in the shape of sea horses or of wrestlers interlocked or winged cupids. One artist had made one of these caskets—which were like the kistai used by the Greeks for ritual purposes—chased with a battle of Amazons,[1] and upon the lid had placed two boys gracefully floating on a pair of swans whose tails formed the handles of the box.

The Etruscan ladies were well versed in the art of dyeing their hair, and Tarquinia had plenty of false blondes. Nothing, however, was more delightful than the custom of carrying a fan and a parasol. And what jewelry, what works of gold and silver the ladies wore! Tarquin noticed upon the breasts of a dark-haired beauty a necklace of rather large disks and threadlike spirals. Another wore a large bracelet made of filigree and granules affixed to the background in exquisite design, a kind of goldwork in which the Etruscan goldsmiths specialized; no one else seemed to know how the granulation of the gold was obtained. The jewelers had recently devised dainty necklaces of braided gold, adorned along the edges with little pendants in the form of heads, palmettes, lotus blossoms. The jewels were set with stones, with mauve beads and enriched by vivid enamels. Rare amber from the Baltic was mounted as brooches; stonecutters worked fine intaglios on the flat side of Egyptian scarabs.

One lady wore an impressive disk-shaped brooch, decorated with a geometrical pattern gently embossed in tiny

---

[1] In the Vatican Museum.

points, although this was a type of ornament that had fallen
into disuse and it was now customary to give them as an offer-
tory to the divinatory priests who wore them upon their vestments.

The wives of the lucumons wore upon their hair elaborate
gold diadems made like rows of sunflower petals, enclosing a
large cameo in the center. Others had earrings of long, pend-
ant shapes; there was, one would say, an abundance, almost
an excess of decoration and richness, perhaps a trace of "bar-
baric" taste—but who could tell? Even the men wore jewelry;
the young fops and the obese plutocrats wore around their
wrists huge bangles studded with precious stones, and their
fingers were heavy with rings.

Still, it was always a joy to share the company of the elegant Etruscan ladies, so easy of manners, so bright of conversation, so different from the forced solemnity of Roman
matrons; and so smart, so refined and attractive! Now, the
young person over there; who might she be, with her chest-
nut hair fastened at the back in a net, her clear profile, the
firm white neck relieved by a heavy gold necklace? Her head
might have been painted on an Attic vase; but the mouth
was truly Etruscan with a bitter line about the full, sensual
lips and the wondrous somber eyes—and she wore on her
right wrist, hanging from a bracelet, a tiny make-up box in
the shape of a woman's head. What a charming little thing!

Someone at the next table was poking fun at the misuse
that was being made of certain Dionysiac "mysteries" introduced by Greek charlatans. "Mere pretexts for holding shocking orgies," said a venerable lady; "orgies that end in dreadful copulations with the participants howling like wolves!"
"And how do you know such details, O venerable lady?" And
everybody laughed with tolerant spirit.

The banquet ended with a musical entertainment. A
troupe of dancers came into the hall, accompanied by lyre
and flute players. A male dancer, a *hister*,[1] performed a coun-

---

[1] Hence the Latin *histrion,* or Roman actor.

try dance, as one could see at rustic fetes in honor of agricultural deities. Soon several guests rose from the couches and joined in the dance. The religious origin of the dance became evident in the abandonment of the ladies to the frenzy of movement, in the ecstatic intoxication expressed by the rigidity of their hands and the expressions on their faces as they threw their heads back. The men seemed to play a secondary role; their movements were more calm; each dancer had an individual part, now and then advancing toward his partner but rarely touching her.[1]

Then a musician played a symphony on the subulo, a new instrument like the flute invented by the Etruscans, with double pipes and a double embouchure, which the players passed from one to the other.

More wine mixed with cinnamon was served; and gay conversations were resumed. Tarquin thought that Rome did not know how to hold a banquet. It was absurd to cast aspersions on the Etruscans, accusing them of sexual aberrations; all lies and slanders, Tarquin thought, when one considered that in Athens those pleasures were current money. Yes, Tarquinia was a great city—he wished he could make his Romans better appreciate the pleasures of life! And before departing he must remember to buy some jewelry and some fine clothes and shoes for his wife and ladies in Rome. And ask the lar of Clusium for the name of the dentist who had made for him such a perfect gold bridge.

---

[1] See the paintings of the "Tomb with the Dining Room" at Tarquinia.

II

Whenever Tarquin returned to Rome from Tarquinia he felt irritated by the evident meanness and dowdiness of his city. He had traveled in his carriage lined with warm furs, along the road that came by the narrow pass of Sutri. It was a landscape dotted with small lakes, like the craters of volcanoes, and the view was both wild and peaceful. At the pass between Lake Bracciano and Lake Vico, in a spur of the wooded hills of Mount Cimino, the landscape opened up steep gorges, with rushing streams of water. The whole scene, under the sun, had the reddish-brown tinge of the tufa stone, against which the green of fields and woods stood out dramatically.

In a desolate place where the junction of two ravines formed a natural amphitheater and from the outer semicircle, almost two-thirds of a mile in diameter, the ground fell in a series of terraces, the people of Sutri had built a range of temple tombs, standing twenty feet high above the shafts in the rocks, which ran deep into the mortuary chambers: the frontages were carved entirely out of the rock, with high triangular gables and rows of columns. The upper edges were topped with figures of warriors and dancers on a line with the top of the cliff, giving the landscape a macabre silhouette.

Tarquin had broken his journey at Caere, a town that

from a low hill stretched like an arm out to the bare seashore; a protruding bastion. It was a wealthy, sophisticated city, which had become a byword for its archaic necropolis that kept expanding remorselessly so that the bright green plain by the sea had gradually changed into a monstrous city of the dead. Many of the tombs at Caere were still erected in the archaic style, the rooms decorated with domestic implements carved in bas-relief on the stone walls and square pillars.

Then, before reaching Rome, Tarquin had made another stop at Veii, to pay his respects to the local lar. Veii was, so to speak, at the gates of Rome; one could see part of the city from it. But ancient Veii was already a fortress surrounded by cyclopean walls when the seven hills in the valley of the Tiber were still inhabited by herdsmen living in huts of mud. Veii had played a decisive part in the early development of the new city by the Tiber, the right bank of which was always called the Etruscan bank. In fact, even at this time, seven Etruscan towns crowned the heights around the city, dominating the valley and the river.

Veii was a splendid city and a great center of art. A little below the plateau on which the city stood, on the very edge of a deep precipice, built on a terrace standing out of the hillside, rose the temple of Apollo, a great shrine for the Etruscans and a marvel of art. The Apollo of Veii was famous for its beauty; a splendid piece of statuary with a harsh, pitiless smile, a figure of Apollo that had an emotional effect. It was a statue of clay, hard clay modeled and then gilded and baked in the kilns of Veii's art factories. Truly, the face of the Apollo of Veii was more beautiful than the abstract Greek figures of Apollo with their empty smiles and with the eyes in ecstatic contemplation. The Apollo of Veii, with his dark, almost swarthy face, his downcast look and the cruel, predatory line of his upturned lips, was moving and frightening—a thing of awe, the expression of the powers of creation throbbing in the strength of the legs poised as though ready to thrust forward. Beneath the thin

garments the muscles were taut; behind the saturnine forehead lurked the mystery of death. The artist who had
modeled this god had put his soul into it—the eagerness, anx-
iousness and impetuosity that is the impelling motive of
every desire and action in men.

It was the work of Vulca, the greatest of Etruscan artists;
and Tarquin made it a point to call at the workshop and see
how the statue of Jupiter, which he had commissioned for
the temple of Jupiter Capitolinus in Rome, was progressing.

Tarquin the Proud was a most handsome man. Tall, of
athletic build and with aristocratic features; a most distinguished man with "the build of a hero." His cheeks were
firm and muscular under a magnificent head of hair, and his
beard made him look like the Jupiter modeled by the artists
of Veii—a noble nose superbly placed above a disdainful
mouth which could, at will, appear sensuous and friendly;
but his brown eyes seemed to intimidate and his appearance
was so naturally imposing and majestic that in the least gestures and the most normal actions there was an air of dignity,
indeed of pride. He was the very embodiment of kingly rank.

Tarquin the Proud had a harsh character. The first act of
his reign had been to purge the senate of the supporters of
Servius, eliminating some by death, some by confiscation, and
removing some by such studied insolence as to drive them
into voluntary exile. He abolished all the laws of Servius,
preserving only the army and the division of the plebs into
classes. In a fit of passion, he had broken the fifty tables of
brass upon which the laws were written and had forbidden
the plebeian festivals and the popular holidays of the Paganalia and Compitalia.

He was, in fact, a man who obeyed no law but his own will
and he had soon become a figure of widespread fear and distrust. He was quite aware of it; but why should he care?
Rome was now two centuries old, a small fraction of the "one
day" that was allotted to her by the gods: and all that Rome
was today, albeit so behind the splendor and culture of the

twelve lucumonies, it was modeled on the Etruscan pattern. Rome was—as his old tutor had taken care to drill into him— what the Etruscans had made her! "Fortunate, indeed, was Rome," he was often saying, "that the Tarquinian dynasty was now firmly established on the throne and had broken the absurd custom of appointing alternatively one Etruscan and one Sabine king!"

Yet, King Tarquin knew that there were rumblings of democratic revolt in his very house. One of the nobles whom his grandfather the Priscus had put to death was Junius, born of Latin stock but Tarquin's own uncle; and with that uncle he had also executed his eldest son, for the Junian house had not only opposed his elevation to the throne but had caballed against him afterward. In the fourth year of his reign Tarquin the Second had been driven to destroy the whole family; he had razed its name from the curiae, and reduced the surviving son, his younger cousin Lucius, to the rank of a plebeian, giving him the name of Brutus.

Lucius Brutus was now deprived of the privileges of his noble birth, although he had been permitted to retain the family wealth.

Brutus had two grown-up sons, whose mother was Vitellia, a patrician lady belonging to a wealthy and influential family. The fact that he was already married at the time he was degraded, and his relationship to the Vitellii, were reasons for the kindness King Tarquin personally showed him; for, as a plebeian, Brutus could not have married into a patrician family.

Brutus was a most peculiar man. Sorely grieving under the fate that had befallen his house at the hands of the Tarquins, he affected isolation from society and asserted the virtue of the simple life of former days, saying that austerity is the companion of solitude. He also tried to give the impression of being a dullard; but all Rome was asking, was he really the dolt he pretended to be?

The harsh treatment suffered by the Junian family had turned Brutus into a fanatical patriot. He fancied that he was creating a character, and openly spoke frantically of his destiny to "overthrow the oppressor" and to revive "the rule of the people." In society and in the forum many people laughed at these tirades of Brutus the idiot and called them a curious affectation; but King Tarquin knew that to the plebs Brutus was a hero and the populace whispered that his very name was an omen, for in the Oscan language Brutus meant "a slave" and was another term for "servius" or "the plebeian."

Had he been wise, King Tarquin often pondered, in giving his degraded cousin the name of Brutus? Now the echo of this very name made King Tarquin turn pale.

Yet, or perhaps because of a superstition, Tarquin had been extremely kind to Brutus. Why had he allowed the young man to retain the cognomen of the degraded family? He had brought him up with his own children, entertained him in the palace and recently he had raised him to a position which it was not lawful for any plebeian to occupy. He had made Lucius Brutus Tribunus Celerum, that was Master of the Royal Guards, head of the curiae, third in rank under the King. This elevation was so exceptional indeed that the patricians had felt it was an act of arbitrary power, and they had complained that the appointment was in contempt of their privileges. Yet, the ancient patricians had suffered the appointment because Lucius Brutus had a right to it by birth, although none by law, and some had seen in it an act of forgiveness and liberality on the part of King Tarquin.

But Brutus himself felt no gratitude, and went on keeping his habitual gloom and taciturnity and talking democratic nonsense.

Tarquin the Proud knew quite well that he was feared by many, and he himself had many fears—in the houses of the die-hards it was whispered that King Tarquin was so suspicious of all mankind that he did not allow his barber to use a razor, and had his hair and beard singed with a live coal! But he was a creator of magnificent plans. He had emulated his grandfather with his stupendous public works, although in their realization he was less considerate of the feelings of his subjects. He had now brought to completion the Cloaca Maxima, and was raising the grandiose temple upon the Capitol for which the Priscus had only been able to collect the material. The ground on which the great temple was being built had been originally taken up with many holy places of the Sabines, which had been founded in the days of King Tatius. But Tarquin the First had consulted the gods by augur; and the gods allowed him to take away all the holy places but the sanctuaries of Youth and Terminus, god of boundaries, which they would not suffer him to move. And the augur said this was a happy omen, for it meant that the youth of the city would never pass away nor it boundaries be moved by the conquest of any enemy.

The augur had spoken the words of consecration—the words that had been spoken by Tarchun when he founded the Temple of Tinia at Tarquinia; the foundation stone had been laid amid flowers and music and sacrifices, by the assembled priesthood and in the presence of all the patriciate, while the populace shouted joyfully. But before the first stone was laid, a human head, still bleeding and warm, was dug out from the soil.[1] The King demanded of the Etruscan augur, Olenus Calenus, what such a spectacle portended. The augur looked at the King, and replied it portended that the people who ruled there should rule all Italy. At these words the foundations which were marked out for the temple were surrounded with fillets and crowns, and those soldiers who had happy-sounding names went in and threw upon the ground branches of olive and other sacred trees. Then came the vestal virgins and children whose parents were both alive, and they bathed the place with fountain water and with water from the river. Tarquinius Priscus sacrificed a bull and a sheep and a pig, and laying the entrails of the victims upon the soil he prayed to Jupiter, Juno and Minerva to bless the place. He touched the garlands in which the sacred corner-

---

[1] Pliny, XXVIII, 2.

stone was bound and raised it by a cord, while all the people
shouted and helped the King. Then the people threw in gold,
silver and copper, that were the metals of Tinia, Talna and
M-n-rva. With similar ceremonial Tarchun and Romulus had
consecrated their first temple.

Now the temple was equal in magnificence to that of Pae-
stum, and the Second Tarquin was justly proud of it. It covered eight acres of ground, facing south toward the Palatine
and the forum. Its circumference was 800 feet, 207 in length
by 192 in breadth,[1] stretching backward to the Tarpeian
Rock, from which the criminals and the enemies of Rome
were hurled to their death. One hundred broad steps
ascended to it, divided by spacious landing places; and the
temple had a nave dedicated to Jupiter, and two aisles, in
which were the shrines and images of Juno and Minerva. The
statue of Jupiter was of clay modeled by an artist of Fregella,
named Turrianus, that meant the Etruscan. The processions
reached the temple by one hundred broad steps divided by
spacious landing spaces; and entered it by large folding doors
of brass, with a magnificent arch, adorned with Tuscan pillars
in three rows, spaced at an interval of fifteen feet and forming a portico along the front with an imposing central entrance, while a single row of pillars extended on each side. It
was, this great temple of Jupiter Capitolinus, a pure Etruscan
fabrication, built and adorned by Etruscan artists, and shaped
and divided according to the rules of the Etruscan Sacred
Books.[2]

Tarquin had indeed employed only Etruscan artists to cast
and mold, to cut the stone and to make the ornaments of
gold, of brass and of wood. For the metope adorning the
frontage Tarquin had ordered a splendid chariot with four
horses to be executed in painted clay by the renowned artists
of Veii; but this was not yet ready.

---

[1] Dionysius.

[2] Dionysius of Halicarnassus, who lived for twenty years in sight of it, wrote
a minute account of its form and proportion. A representation of the temple
of Jupiter can be seen on the coins of Vespasian and Domitian, by whom it
was restored.

In commemoration of the head that had been found in the soil the name of the hill was changed from Tarpeia, and was henceforth called the Capitol, or Caput-Toli, the head of Tolus; and the temple was named to Jupiter Capitolinus. Tolus, alas, was an unfortunate Aerarian of Vulci, who had incurred the King's displeasure.

Tarquin considered this great temple of Jupiter Capitolinus as his most splendid monument; and on the day it was inaugurated, he ascended to it dressed in his embroidered tunic, crowned with the golden crown, preceded by his heralds and lictors carrying before him the double ax in the bundles of rods as the sacred symbol of power. The bronze plating of his new chariot was decorated with designs of plants, vulture-headed lions, sphinxes and winged horses: it was the chariot of triumph. Indeed, Tarquin had already decreed that there would ascend, forever, all the victorious embrators in their triumphal processions, with their bodies painted with vermilion, as with vermilion was covered Jupiter's face in festive days; and that they should wear the very clothes of Jupiter Optimus Maximus, the triumphal robe, the scepter and the golden diadem of oak leaves, which were kept in the temple. And into this temple every year a great nail would be hammered to mark the number of city years, not on Rome's birthday which was the sacred birthday of Tarquinia, but on the Ides of September, when the Praetor Maximus would hammer a nail into the right wall of the cell of Jupiter Capitolinus.

The temple of Jupiter was never changed, and when, centuries afterward, the Romans wanted to enlarge it and change its form, the augur answered that Jove neither changed his form nor altered the bounds of his habitation.[1]

Subsequently, outside the temple was placed a great figuration of a wolf suckling the twins Romulus and Remus, founders of Rome.[2]

---

[1] Tacitus, III, 71.

[2] This wolf was made at Veii: it is now called "The Capitoline Wolf," and is preserved in the Conservatori Museum, Rome.

III

One day, soon after the temple of Jupiter Capitolinus was opened, a strange woman of patrician rank and priestly dignity arrived in Rome. She had brought with her nine books, which she offered to the King as the Libri Fatales of his kingdom and temple.

The woman asked a very high price for the books, which appeared to be written in verse upon palm leaves. King Tarquin refused the offer, and ordered the woman to leave.

Exactly one year later, the woman returned. She said she had burned three of her books, and offered the remaining six to King Tarquin for the same price. Tarquin again refused, and told the woman that his augurs knew all he wished to know concerning the future of his kingdom.

But the woman returned the following year. She had now only three books left, for which she still asked the same price.

King Tarquin felt that there was something preternatural in the woman's behavior. He gave the books to the augurs, ordering them to examine the volumes.

The books were written in the Etruscan language, mingled with Greek maxims of wisdom, which the augurs believed to be from Cuma, and other oracles that they pronounced to be written in hieroglyphic characters.

After much deliberation, the augurs advised King Tarquin to buy the books. Tarquin ordered that the Libri Fatales should be kept in a special cell of the temple of Jupiter; and he appointed two priests, called the Duumviri, to take care of them; the augurs were to consult them in hours of national need.[1] The woman who had so persistently brought the books to Rome became known as the Sibylla.[2]

For the next seven years Tarquin was engaged in wars, renewing his league with Etruria, the Latins and the Hernicans, and bringing to heel the Volsci that threatened his dominions.

He made friends with the chief men among the Latins, and gave his daughter in marriage to Octavius Mamilius of Tusculum. He was now very powerful among the Latins, and when Turnus Herdonius of Aricia dared to speak against him in the great assembly of the Latins and their allies at Feronia, contending that the Latins should not suffer an Etruscan to rule over them, Tarquin accused him of conspiracy. He procured false witnesses to confirm the charge, attributing Turnus' aversion to his disappointment that Tarquin had refused him his daughter in marriage and married her instead to Mamilius of Tusculum, who was a sort of half-kindred blood, for Tusculum was in its remote origin an Etruscan colony. Turnus was brought before the assembly in chains. His partisans attempted to draw swords. To avoid a confusion the Latin assembly judged Turnus guilty of wanting to change the government; and without allowing him a word in defense, sentenced him to be thrown in the reservoir

---

[1] In after years, the Libri Fatales were called the Sibylline Books; and for many centuries the people of Rome had a superstitious belief in regard to their sayings and prophecies.

[2] In later times, the Romans collected, besides these books, all the Greek prophecies and those of Cuma and Ethiopia, and probably many more sacred books. The Duumviri were made priests of Apollo, in order to make them similar to the priests of Delphi. Among the prophecies of the Sibylline Books there was one saying that the Parthians would never submit to Rome except to a Roman king, and this was one of the thoughts that weighed most on Caesar's mind when, a few months before he was assassinated, he was planning, at Cleopatra's prompting, his Persian campaign.

of Feronia and a hurdle placed over him until he was
drowned.

After this, the forty-seven chiefs of Latium and their allies
the Hernicans and the Volsci acclaimed Tarquin to be their
sole commander, and followed him to war against Gabii. The
war lasted seven years.

This well-fortified city, stronghold of rebels, would not
yield. Tarquin's third son, Sextus, undertook therefore to
capture it by fraud. He feigned to take sides with the plebs
against his father King Tarquin, upon which the King ordered him to be whipped. Sextus retreated to Gabii, apparently in shame, pleading to be admitted on the old grounds
of isopoly with Rome. The Gabine and Roman malcontents welcomed him, because he was known to be a man of
great military talent; and Sextus led them against King Tarquin with constant success, until they elected him their general and dictator.

At this point Sextus sent a secret messenger to his father to
know how he should act further. Tarquin, instead of answering, took the messenger into his garden, and walking on in
silence, he cut off the heads of all the tallest poppies. He then
told the messenger that he could give no advice, but to be
sure to tell his son what he had done in the garden.

Sextus understood that he was to rid himself quietly of all
the most important exiles in Gabii; and accordingly he got
the Gabine senate to ruin or kill them. And so, at the end of
seven years, Sextus made an honorable peace for Gabii with
King Tarquin the Proud, securing to them their own laws,
privileges and independent jurisdiction on the payment of a
moderate tribute, giving to them the Roman franchise. This
treaty of peace, written on a bull's hide and stretched on a
wooden shield, was hung up in the temple of Jupiter Fides,
which had been erected by King Numa.[1]

Now King Tarquin was well advanced in years; but his
will never flagged. His powers were absolute. War, peace,

---

[1] This shield was still preserved under the Empire.

treaties, alliances he contracted and dissolved at will, without the sanction of the senate and people. Of his four sons, three were governors of strong foreign cities, Signia, Antium and Gabii; and the fourth was a lucumo or assistant to his father in Rome. The whole of Sabina, Latium, Volscia and Tyrrhenia were at peace with Rome. From his palace near the new temple of Jupiter, King Tarquin ruled the senate absolutely, and made the proud curia submit to a plebeian tribune, Brutus, because it was his will and whim to give them one.

Nevertheless, though the peace was outward it was not inward. The temple of Janus was not shut, King Tarquin was not secure nor was he happy. The contending and opposing parties of patricians and plebeians were hating and struggling against each other.

Rome was no longer the city that Tarquinius Priscus had contemplated from the Janiculum. It was already a fine city, full of building and renovating activity.

All the riverside was a vast market in the modern sense, with the Forum Boarium an open cattle market, with shops all around it. And the Forum Romanum was now the center of political and judicial business, as well as of social life.

From the early hours of the morning the forum, enclosed at the northwestern end by the Capitoline Hill with its double summit and the great temple of Jupiter facing toward the Aventine, was crowded with bustling people, intent on political affairs, or in the law courts, or in banking transactions, or merely passing away the time in idle gossip.

Perhaps the greatest novelty was the shops of the argentarii, the moneylenders or bankers of Rome. They had been, originally, only money changers; but with the expansion of trade, a new class of financiers and speculators was formed to facilitate the interchange of money between other cities and other countries without the handling of cumbersome coinage. The argentarii were all men of the knightly or equites class, as senators were not supposed by law to engage in business that would take them out of the city—and, needless to say, their business was conducted by proxy!

The forum had originally been in a valley, formed by a stream which flowed down between the Esquiline and the Quirinal beyond it, and joined the Tiber on the other side by the way of the Velabrum. Now after the completion of the cloaca which drained the stream, the forum was extended and developed, the lower part of what had been the stream had become a crowded street, the Vicus Tuscus, leading to the Velabrum and to the cattle market.

Close to the entry of the forum was the charming round temple of Vesta, where the sacred fire was kept burning by its guardians the vestal virgins, and nearby was their convent, the Atrium Vestae, and also the Regia, residence of the Pontifex Maximus, in whose potestas the vestal virgins were. These three buildings constituted the religious center of the oldest part of Rome.

But at the farther end of the forum were the rostra from which orators addressed the crowds of idlers on political subjects. To the right of the rostra was the comitium, or assembly place of the people. There was also the curia, the meeting hall of the senate.

And toward the Capitol, beyond the famous temple or gate of the double-headed Janus standing at the other entrance to the forum from the Argiletum and the Porta Esquilina, lay the foot of the Clivus Capitolinus, where the Via Sacra turned to ascend the Capitol. Below, to the south, was the temple of Saturn, which was used as the treasury or aerarium of the city. Thus, at this end of the forum under the Capitol, were situated all the public offices, facing the ancient religious buildings.

Life in Rome, so far, had been very simple. But now—said the reactionaries—after the new reforms of King Tarquin, it tended to become more complex, and also more difficult. The burden of capitation made the moneylenders more prosperous; their banks in the forum did brisk business, and many were the bags of money carried away as a result of the heart-breaking cost of mortgages on the land. Tradesmen and business people traveled into Etruria and brought back rich fabrics and beautiful goods for the houses of the rich, and also tales of the refined life they saw in the splendid foreign cities. Besides, there was Veii, a short distance from Rome, a mere three hours' journey by horse carriage. The Etruscans lived there in fine style, and the wealthy people in Rome were copying them.

But no similar goods could be produced in Rome; and commercially, as otherwise, Rome was every year more completely dependent on Etruria.

The elders deplored the self-indulgent luxurious life at the court of King Tarquin; they deplored that the new patricians had taken to living in the higher districts of the city, leaving the lower part to the plebs and the bottom stratum of population. This was not entirely so, for poor people no doubt lived on the Aventine, the Caelian and parts of the Esquiline. But the Palatine was certainly an aristocratic quarter; the Carinae, the height looking down on the valley where the Colosseum now stands, had many rich houses, and many more were being built on the Quirinal. All the working classes were crammed in the narrow alleys leading down from these heights to the forum, such as the Suburra between Esquiline and Quirinal, and the Argiletum farther down near the forum, where the shoemakers lived.

The rich were now having houses built that were almost as large and as grand as the palace of the King himself—houses in which the atrium was adorned with a beautifu colonnade, and some had built behind the atrium and exedra a series of open reception rooms convenient for many pur poses. The rooms were now furnished entirely in the Etrus can style, with imported knickknacks and *objets d'art;* the dining couches in the triclinium were copied from the Etrus can, and soon ladies were sharing the couches with the guests in the true immoral fashion of Etruria! Everybody knew that this fashion was already followed at court, but Kin

Tarquin had sufficient tact to keep the ladies out when he had the more venerable senators dining at the palace.

Beneath all this there was a deep hatred of the Etruscans and of the Tarquinian dynasty in particular. "We are Latins," the Quirites and the Sabines said with contemptuous disdain, "why should we be treated as a dependency of the Etruscan League?" And those Tarquinian kings, they said, were bad enough for anyone. What had they done for Rome? Built some extravagant buildings, and at what price! For peoples are always inclined to decry their kings, and attribute to themselves whatever power and progress have been achieved by the sagacity of their rulers.

There was a strong feeling against the new senators created by Tarquin—"Men," they said, "who are there only because they have been given the title to be there by King Tarquin." The hatred was directed most strongly against King Tarquin —and all this latent opposition was encouraged by Tarquin's dark and scheming nephew Brutus who bore him a hatred that nothing could diminish.

BOOK FOUR

THE
RAPE
OF
LUCRECE

I

At what point can one fix the birth of democratic thought in a country? One might, perhaps, say that the principle of democracy is inborn in man. The people of Rome, since the time of Tarquin the First, were divided into the three tribes of the Ramnes, Titics and Luceres: they belonged to those races and circumstances had brought them together. Each of these tribes was divided into ten smaller bodies called curiae; so that the whole people consisted of thirty curiae. These same divisions were, in the army, represented by the thirty centuries which made up one legion, just as the three tribes were represented by the three centuries of cavalry.

It would be more exact to say that the union of ten curiae formed the tribe, for the state had grown out of the fusion of certain original elements, which were neither the tribes nor the curiae, but gentes or houses, which made up the curiae, a union of several families bound together by the joint performance of certain religious rites. Nearly eight centuries later the newly born Christian Church would retain the idea and the name of curiae as the basis of its organization.

Thus the state was made up of families, and from the earliest times the family consisted of members and dependents. The original inhabitants of the city were either members of families and, if so, members of a curia and consequently of a tribe; or they were dependents on a family, in which case their relation went no further than the immediate aggregate of families, and they had no connection with the curia and the tribe and, lastly, with the state. The members of families were the original citizens of Rome; their dependents were the clients. The clients were something to their patrons, but to the state they were nothing.

In a rapidly growing city, strangers must come to live in the land; or the inhabitants of a neighboring land might be conquered and united to their conquerors as subject people. These new populations had only a political relation to the state and its citizens: they represented political subjection. They were an inferior population, and yet they owned property, they regulated their own public and domestic affairs and fought in the army of what was now the common country, albeit they were not citizens and could not intermarry with the original citizens, and belonged to no curia and to no tribe, and consequently they had no share in the state's government.

Such an inferior population, personally free but politically subject, not slaves and yet not citizens, was the plebs. It was in the plebs that the seed of democracy matured; and the plebs, the mass of common people, remained throughout the centuries the determining factor of political life in Rome.

The plebs were mostly conquered Latins. They had received grants of a portion of their former lands, to be held by them as Roman subjects; moreover, those who had moved to Rome were assigned as residence the Aventine Hill. The Aventine—the name of which became antonomastic of democratic isolation—was outside the walls of Rome, although quite near the city, and the plebs, like the Pfahlbürger of the Middle Ages, were people not admitted to live within the city but enjoyed its protection.

The state, therefore, was composed only of full citizens, that is, the members of the curiae. The assembly of the people was the assembly of the curiae; and the senate, consisting of two hundred senators chosen in equal members from the two higher tribes of the Ramnes and Tities, was the smaller council. Within the walls every citizen had a right of appeal to the King, or to his judges against the sentence of his peers; that is, every citizen could appeal to the great council of the curiae. The King had his demesne lands, and in war he received his portion of the conquered land as well as of the booty.

The greatness of the monarchy under the Tarquinian kings was attested by the colossal public works completed in that period and by the famous treaty with Carthage, preserved to us by Polybius.[1] Under the last two kings, the city had reached the limits which it retained through the most flourishing times of the Empire—centuries later; and the walls of Servius continued to be the walls of Rome down to the Emperor Aurelian, eight hundred years later. Those walls enclosed the seven hills.

Tarquin the First had built the line of rampart, and the mighty masonry with which the bank of the Tiber was built up could be compared to the works of the Babylonian kings along the banks of the Euphrates. Such works as the Cloaca Maxima were evidence of a strong government, which had at its command the whole resources of the people; but they also pointed to a rule based upon a considerable extent of dominions.

Indeed, from the treaty with Carthage it appeared that the whole coast of Latium was already subject to the sovereignty of Rome: Ardea, Antium, Circeii, Terracina, were mentioned as subject allies of Rome; and Rome could not be mistress of the whole coast of Latium without some authority over the interior. Moreover, Rome was the acknowledged head of the Latin cities with a power resembling the sovereignty of Athens over her allies.

---

1 Polybius, however, asserts that the language of that treaty was so unlike the Latin of his own time that even those who understood it best found something in it which they could scarcely explain. Equally, the hymns of the Fratres Arvales—the Brotherhood of Husbandry—required to be interpreted at the time of Cicero like a foreign language.

Thus Rome was now the seat of a great monarchy extending over the whole of Latium on the one side, and possessing some considerable territory in Etruria on the other. And all this power was due to the last three kings, all of Etruscan origin.

But the two Tarquins, and especially Tarquin the Proud, had dared to impinge upon the old constitution; hence the agitation in Rome for a return to the older state of things.

The new constitution had served to strengthen an absolute monarchy. The old one was an oligarchy; it could be called "democratic" only inasmuch as it regarded the relations of the citizens, or of the curiae and tribes, to each other. The first changes, made by Tarquinius Priscus, had, with only slight modification, preserved this character. Tarquin the First had doubled the number of senators, or rather the patrician houses, which involved a corresponding increase in the number of senators. But the houses newly ennobled were distinguished from the old ones by the qualification of lesser houses, and their senators did not vote till after the senators of the greater houses had given their votes.

Tarquin the Proud had proposed to double the number of the tribes, dividing his newly created houses into three tribes, to stand beside the three ancient tribes of the Ramnes, the Tities and the Luceres. This would have radically altered the composition of the army, as the military divisions of old went along with the civil divisions, the tribes being the centuries of the army; and if three new tribes were added, it involved also the addition of three new centuries of knights or cavalry.

The objection of the old tribes, however, was a religious one; and it was strong enough to force the King to modify his plan. No new tribes were created and consequently no new centuries; but the new houses were enrolled in the three old centuries, so as to form a second division in each, and thus to remain inferior in dignity to the old houses in every relation to the state.

Yet, Tarquin had no alternative to this constitutional

change. He was an Etruscan; he was a foreigner. The mere growth of the Roman state, in the natural course of things, would have multiplied the houses, with new families who had risen to wealth and were, moreover, of noble blood in their former country, but were excluded in Rome from the curiae and the rights of citizenship. The time had come to open to them the doors of the commonwealth. A foreign king, ambitious to add to the strength of his kingdom, could not put off the decision.

The constitutional changes touched one religious point: Tarquin increased the number of the vestal virgins from four to six, so that each of the three tribes now had two vestal virgins. But in the additions made to the senate and to the army, the new citizens were numerically more than a third of the old ones; and, anyway, the number of new distinguished families, of whatever origin, was so great that an extension of the rights of citizenship was almost unavoidable.

These changes, however, went no further than to admit these families into the aristocracy, leaving the character and privileges of the aristocracy, with regard to the plebs or mass of the population, precisely as before.

The real changes came soon afterward; and it was the establishment of a new constitution on totally different principles. They were changes that gave cause to the plebs to raise the cry of regret for "the just laws of good King Servius, the democratic King." For King Servius, who had ascended the throne to the exclusion of the grandsons of the old King, to propitiate the plebs had created a new and different people out of the large mass of inhabitants of Rome who had no political existence.

The principle of an aristocracy is equality within its own body, and ascendancy over all the rest of the community. Opposed to this is the system which subjects no part of the community to another, and gives a portion of power to all—not an equal portion, but one graduated according to a certain standard, the standard of property. This system does away with distinctions of birth, and it creates distinctions of property. It creates the middle class.

The three old tribes had been divisions of birth, for each was made up of the houses of the curiae, and no man could belong to the tribe without belonging to a curia or to a house, nor could a stranger become member of a house except by adoption, by which rite he was made as one of the same race and therefore a lawful worshiper of the same gods. Each of these tribes owned a portion of the old territory of Rome, which was called the Ager Romanus. But now, many others had come to live under the Roman King without belonging to the old tribes, and had received grants of land beyond the limits of the ancient Ager. A new division, therefore, was made of them; and the whole territory of Rome, except the Capitol—that was holy ground—was divided into thirty tribes, four for the city and twenty-six for the country, containing all the people who were not members of the old houses, and classing them according to their property. These thirty new tribes corresponded to the thirty curiae of the houses, for the houses used to assemble divided into thirty; and now the commons were to meet in the assembly of their tribes, as the houses met in the assembly of the curiae.

There were created, therefore, two houses of parliament, existing alongside each other, two estates distinct and independent of each other. They could not act as joint legislative chambers, for the old curiae still regarded themselves as representing exclusively the Roman people.[1]

But there was one way in which it was practicable to unite them into one great body, and this was when they marched out to war. And the peculiar constitution of the comitia or centuries was a device for uniting the old tribes and the new plebs into a national assembly in their capacity of soldiers, without shocking prejudices and privileges.

In order to secure in this great assembly a preponderance of plebs, it was indispensable to make a change in the mili-

---

[1] It was analogous to the House of Lords and the House of Commons of England's ancient Constitution.

tary organization and tactics. In all aristocracies, and more so in ancient times, the ruling classes fought on horseback or in chariots, and the people or the mercenaries fought on foot. The cavalry service had been cultivated, brought to a fine military art; the infantry was neglected. The nobles were well-armed and carefully trained; the foot soldiery was ill-armed and often ill-disciplined.

The first great step was to raise the status of the infantry—to give the common people a sense of importance in defense of the state: to train the infantry to resist enemy cavalry, to form into massed groups, and to arm them with pikes, instead of swords or javelins. Thus was born the phalanx order of battle, which was copied from Greece, where it was in general use. It was well known in Italy through the Greek colonies. Its introduction into the Roman army made the infantry more important than the cavalry; and the people forming the infantry would henceforth assert a greater right in the state's affairs. Moreover, the phalanx order of battle was giving individual importance to a great number of the less wealthy commoners who could not supply themselves with complete armor, while on the other hand it suggested a natural distinction between them and their richer fellows, and thus established property as the standard of political power, the only power which can compete, in any society, with the aristocratic power of birth.

In the deep phalanx only the front ranks needed to be completely armed; the rear ranks could neither reach nor be reached by the enemy, and they only served to add weight to the charge.

The first reformer, King Servius, had found the knights divided into three centuries of cavalry, each of which contained two centuries, the first and the second. The description of three centuries was merely a fiction to keep up the old form of the state, preventing the six actual centuries from being acknowledged as such in name. The Servian change extended to the name as well as the reality, and the three double centuries became now the six votes—*sex suffragia*—of the new united assembly. To these, which contained all the members of the old houses, were now added twelve new centuries, formed, on the Greek model, from the richest members of the community who continued, however, to belong to the thirty tribes of the commoners.

The foot soldiers, or plebs, were then organized. All who owned property sufficient to qualify them for serving in the ranks were divided into four classes. The first contained all whose property amounted to one hundred and fifty thousand pounds weight of copper. (Copper was taken as the basic valuation of property, as it had been the first currency since early times, because it was found in immense quantities and even in large masses of pure metal on the surface of the soil. The small value of copper in Etruria, and consequently in Rome, was shown not only by the large size of early coins, which, at first, were a full pound in weight, but also by the price of the war horse, which, according to regulation of Servius, was ten thousand pounds of copper.)

The soldiers of the first class were to provide themselves with the arms used in the front ranks of the phalanx: the coat of mail, the greaves, the helmet and the round buckler, all of bronze, plus the sword and the peculiar weapon of the heavy infantry, the long pike. These troops had to bear the brunt of every battle, and they were the flower of the state soldiery; so their weight in the great military assembly was in proportion—eighty centuries, forty of younger men between fifteen years of age and forty-five, and forty of elders between forty-five and sixty—the first to serve in the field, the second to defend the city.

The second class included those whose property was below one hundred thousand pounds of copper but exceeded seventy-five thousand. They formed twenty centuries, ten of younger men, ten of elders; and they were allowed to dispense with the coat of mail, and wore the large oblong shield, or scutum, instead of the round clipeus of the first rank. The third class was composed of a like number of centuries, again equally divided into younger men and elders. They were not obliged to wear the greaves or the coat of mail; they were men whose property stood between seventy-five and fifty thousand pounds of copper. The fourth class was made up again of twenty centuries whose qualification was twenty-five thousand pounds of copper, and whose soldiers were required to go to war armed merely with pike and javelin. These four classes of infantry composed the phalanx. But a fifth class, divided into thirty centuries and consisting of men whose property was between twenty-five thousand and twelve thousand five hundred pounds of copper, formed the light infantry. They were to provide themselves only with darts and slings. The poorest citizens, whose property fell short of twelve thousand five hundred pounds, were considered supernumeraries in this division. Those who had more than fifteen hundred pounds of copper were still reckoned among the taxpayers, and were formed into two centuries called the accensi and velati; they followed the army without bearing arms, being only required to step into the places of those who fell, and in the meantime acting as orderlies to the centurions and decurions.

Below these came the century of the proletarii, who paid no taxes and had, in ordinary times, no military duties; but in great emergencies arms were furnished to them by the government and they were called out as an extraordinary levy. One century more included all whose property was less than three hundred and seventy-five pounds, and who were called capite censi; from them no military service was at any time required.

There were three more centuries of a different character, not defined by the amount of property but by the nature of their occupation: the carpenters or smiths (fabrorum), the hornblowers or cornicines, and the trumpeters or tubicines.[1] The first were attached to the centuries of the first class, the other two to the fourth.

The clients of the patricians had no vote, and they were enrolled in the army according to the amount of their prop-

---

[1] Cicero calls them *liticines*.

erty. However, they followed their lords in the field, and formed a sort of feudal army quite distinct from the national army of the commoners, like the retainers of the nobles in the Middle Ages as distinguished from the free burghers of the cities.

This was the composition of the comitia of the centuries. Being a military organization, they met outside the city, in the Field of Mars; were called together by the blast of the horn, not by the lictors, and the name was the Army of the City, Exercitus Urbanus.

It is obvious that this constitution tended to give the chief power of the state to the commoners, and especially to the richer classes among them, who fought in the first ranks of the phalanx. For, as Aristotle said, the chief power was apt to be possessed by that class of the people whose military services were the most important, such as happened in Athens when the navy became its great support and strength, and the governments became democratic because the ships were manned by the poorer classes.

King Servius had made other democratic reforms. As he made the commoners an order of the state, he gave them judges out of their own body to try all civil causes, judges that in a later period were called the centumviri.

He also instituted the festivals of Paganalia and Compitalia. The first were held every year in the country, in the strongholds on high ground which had been fixed as general shelters for cattle and countryfolk in case of invasion. During those festivals every man, woman and child paid a certain sum to the priests, which gave the amount of the whole population. For the same purpose of yearly census, everyone living in the city paid a fixed sum at the temple of Juno Lucina for every birth in the family and another sum at the temple of Venus Libitina for every death, and a third sum at the temple of youth for every son who came of military age. The Compitalia in the city were yearly festivals in honor of the lares, or guardians, celebrated at all the compita, or places where several streets met.

King Servius had also driven out the patricians from their unjust occupation of public land, and ordered that the property only and not the person of a debtor should be liable for the payment of a debt. It was also said that King Servius had drawn out a scheme of popular government whereby two magistrates, chosen every year, were to exercise the supreme power, and these two magistrates were to be chosen one from the houses and the other from the commons.

But now King Tarquin had swept away the institutions of Servius and prevented the development of the new society. The aristocratic brotherhoods served him more zealously than the legal assembly of the curiae; and Tarquin recklessly crushed the liberties of the commons and even destroyed the tables upon which the laws of Servius were written, abolishing the system of the census and consequently the arrangement of the classes and with them the military organization of the phalanx. He formed his army out of a small portion of the people, and employed the bulk of the plebs in his spectacular public works, the Capitoline temple and the completion of the Cloaca Maxima. The army consisted of his allies, the Latins and Hernicans, in much greater proportion than of Romans.

Another cause of general discontent was the taxes, that worked on the system of capitation: every citizen, from the noblest knight to the humblest workman, had to pay a tax according to his assessed property; and under this system privileges and reliefs always worked in favor of the richer and the higher in rank. Many patricians went scot-free; the plebs were mercilessly mulcted. For instance, the priests claimed exemption on the ground that the temples' treasure was property of the gods, and they even managed to appear good patriots by offering a "voluntary" amount. The biggest landowners also managed to reach a compromise by agreeing to a settled sum.

Moreover, owing to the association with the National League of Etruria, Rome was an open market for all Etruscan goods and products; her industrial production was nil, while her manufactured goods could not compete with the Etruscan, which were far superior in quality and enjoyed the advantage of a long-established trade.

Thus it was not surprising that Tarquin was hated by the commoners and by all who were good and noble among the ancient houses. Both orders desired his overthrow. Many of the nobles were now saying that only the expulsion of the King and his family could restore the union of all the people as an equal order, free, well-organized and well-armed for expansion. And the poorer classes saw a prophet and a leader in the aristocrat who had been lowered to the plebeian level—Lucius Junius Brutus. No one could imagine that the fruit of a revolution would be an exclusive and tyrannical democracy.

II

One day, while Tarquin was sacrificing at his domestic altar in the chapel of the palace, a snake crawled up from under the altar, devoured all the offerings upon the altar, and terrified the household.

It was, Tarquin thought, a period of bad omens. Some weeks previously he had to pass sentence upon a vestal virgin who had broken her vow of virginity; and this, a thing that had not occurred for a very long time, seemed to him a sure sign of ill omen. For the rules governing the vestals were still those prescribed by old King Numa, and the sentence upon the transgressor could only be the horrible death of being buried alive.

Numa prescribed that the vestals, the keepers of the Sacred Fire, should take a vow of virginity for thirty years. The first ten they were to spend in learning their duties, the second ten in performing them, and the remaining ten in teaching and instructing others. The whole term being completed, it was lawful for the vestals to marry or, leaving the sacred order and the nunnery, to choose any condition of life that pleased them; but few made use of it, and for those who did marry, it was noticed that the change was not a happy one.

For the observance of these strict rules Numa had granted

the vestals great privileges and prerogatives. They had the right to make a will during the lifetime of their own fathers; they could freely administer their affairs and properties without a guardian, a privilege that was granted only to married women who were mothers of three children; and when they went out, they had the fasces carried before them, and should they meet a criminal on his way to execution, his life was saved. Any man who approached the chair in which a vestal was carried through the streets was put to death. Only the high priest could punish them for minor faults; in the seclusion of the vestals' nunnery, the high priest would scourge the naked offender with a curtain drawn between.

But the vestal virgin who broke her vow must be buried alive near the gate called Collina, where a little mound of earth stood, within the city. Under the mound was a narrow room, to which one descended by a ladder; and here the executioner would prepare a bed and light a lamp and leave a small quantity of bread, water, a pail of milk and some oil, so that a woman who had been consecrated and devoted to the most sacred service of religion might not be said to die of starvation.

The day of the execution—now Tarquin recalled—the culprit was brought into the forum, tied inside a litter, which was all enclosed so that nothing she uttered might be heard. Along the streets the people moved out of the way at the sight of the litter, and the few relatives that followed it were like mourners escorting a hearse. There was nothing more frightful.

Then the litter was taken to the dreadful mound. The officers loosened the cords, and the high priest raised his hands to heaven and prayed aloud. Then he brought out the prisoner, shrouded from head to foot, and placed her upon the steps that led down to the dungeon, averting his face. After the condemned had gone down, the ladder was drawn up and a quantity of earth was heaped over the entrance, to prevent its being distinguished from the rest of the mound. Thus was punished the vestal virgin who had broken her vow of virginity—but it had been a most appalling spectacle.

And now there was this new bad omen—a serpent coming up from underneath the altar in the very palace.

Tarquin felt much troubled. He knew only too well that portentous omens often required skillful manipulation to materialize; but precisely because of this, he wondered who was interested in causing such an omen to appear. Moreover, no Etruscan would lightly dismiss a bad omen: Tarquin's soul was cradled in superstition—the superstition that moves men more deeply than any true belief. What was the meaning of this ugly portent, even if it came from some persons rather than from a god?

Soon after this, Tarquin had a dream. He saw a terrible pair of eagles—the royal bird of his house!—building a nest in a palm tree in his garden; the birds flew away in search of food, and when they returned they found their eaglets tossed out of the nest and their place occupied by ugly vultures that drove off the two royal birds.

Tarquin had yet another dream. Two rams, sprung from one sire, were brought to him to select before the altar; he chose the finest, and immediately the other flew at him, pushing him with its horns and driving him away.

In those very days the sun changed its course, and the day seemed to run from west to east.[1]

Three omens, all bad—and three was a fatal number in the Etruscan numerology. Tarquin consulted the haruspices, and they told him to beware of a man who was of his own blood and as stupid as a sheep in his actions.

Who could this man be? Tarquin thought of Brutus, but he could not imagine real danger from him, for no patrician would ever conspire to place a plebeian on the throne, and unless the Junian house should again take its own place among the Ramnes, no other royal family but the Tarquinians would rule in Rome.

---

[1] Cicero, *De Divinatione*, I, 22.

Yet, this time King Tarquin did not feel satisfied with the interpretations of his Etruscan soothsayers; and he decided to send a mission to Delphi, to consult the oracle that was sacred to a god acknowledged by the Etruscans themselves.

A solemn embassy was fitted out, and the Agyllans—who had recently received from the oracle at Delphi consolatory advice about their murdered prisoners—were ordered to be guides to the embassy. The embassy was headed by two of Tarquin's sons, Titus who was governor of Antium and Aruns the governor of Signia; and Brutus was sent with them to bear them company, as the highest officer who could be spared from Rome—Brutus the dullard, who would eat wild figs with honey, and who might in his witless mind have engineered the omen of the snake under the palace altar.

The party traveled to Delphi and duly arrived at the temple, of which they had never seen the equal. For the temple had been recently rebuilt by the Alcmaeonidae, the old temple having been destroyed by fire, and the sum of three hundred talents had been spent in the new building, partly taken from the treasure of the old temple and partly contributed by all the countries inhabited by Greeks. The restoration was put into the hands of the Corinthian architect Spintharus, who carried it out in a more splendid style than was originally agreed, building the front of the temple of Parian marble instead of limestone. The groups of sculpture in the two pediments represented, on the eastern side, Apollo with Artemis, Leto and the Muses; on the western side, Dionysus with the Thyades and the setting sun, for Dionysus was worshiped here in winter during the imagined absence of Apollo. These statues were all by Praxias and Androsthenes.

On account of its vast extent, the temple was a hypaethral building; that is, there was no roof over the space occupied by the temple proper. The exterior was built in Doric style and the interior Ionic. On the walls of the pronaos were engraved short texts in letters of gold, attributed to the Seven

Wise Men of Thebes, and one of these was the celebrated
"Know Thyself."

In the temple proper stood the golden statue of Apollo,
and in front of it the sacrificial hearth with the eternal fire.
Near this was a globe of marble covered with fillets, sym-
bolizing the omphalos, or center of the earth. In earlier times
two eagles had stood at its side, representing the two eagles
which the legend said had been sent by Zeus at the same moment from the eastern and western ends of the world; but
these eagles were carried off during the Phocian war and their
place was now filled by two eagles in mosaic on the floor. Behind this space was the inner shrine, much lower, looking
like a cavern over a cleft in the ground.

The three messengers of King Tarquin had wandered
within the spacious precincts, filled with admiration at the
great number of chapels, statues, votive offerings and treasure
houses, in which all suppliants deposited their gifts, especially
the tithes of the booty taken in war. And there, too, was the
council chamber of the Delphians. Before the entrance to the
temple rose the great altar for burnt offerings, and the golden
tripod, dedicated by the Greeks after the battle of Plataea, on
a rich pedestal of gleaming brass representing a snake in three
coils. Through the courts moved the hierodules, who were in
charge of menial services; but the rites of the temple, as well
as the management of its vast properties, were in the hands
of the chapter of priests chosen from the most noble Delphian
families, at their head the five Hosioi, or consecrated ones.

The oracle sat in the cleft of the earth in the innermost
sanctuary. From it dense vapors arose, which had the power
of causing ecstasy. Over the cleft stood a lofty golden tripod;
on this was a circular slab, upon which the seat of the prophetess was ceremoniously placed. The prophetess, who was
called the Pythia, used to be in earlier times a maiden of
honorable birth; now she was a woman of over fifty, yet wearing a girl's dress in memory of the earlier custom. In the
earliest times the Pythia ascended the tripod only once a year,
on the birthday of Apollo, the seventh of the Delphian spring

month Bysios. Now the Pythia prophesied every day, provided the day itself and the omens were not unfavorable.

The three messengers of Tarquin offered their sacrifices adorned with laurel crowns and fillets of wool. The Pythia washed and purified herself, then she entered the sanctuary, wearing golden ornaments in her hair and dressed in flowing robes. She drank some water of the fountain Cassotis, which flowed into the shrine; tasted the fruit of the old bay tree that grew in the chamber, and then she took her seat. No one was present but a priest, called the Prophet, who would explain the words that the Pythia uttered in her ecstasy, and put them into metric form, generally hexameters.

The three young men performed all that King Tarquin had bidden them to do; then they asked the oracle: "O Lord Apollo, tell us, which of us shall be King in Rome?" The voice came from the Pythia: "Whichever of you shall first kiss his mother."

So the two sons of Tarquin agreed to draw lots between themselves to decide which of them should first kiss their mother when they returned to Rome; and they further agreed to keep the oracle secret from their brothers Sextus and Lucius.

But before leaving the shrine, Brutus presented as his offering his staff, emblem of his baton as Tribunus Celerum, and which, Brutus said to the god Apollo, was a likeness of himself, for indeed the staff, though it seemed of such plain cornel wood, unadorned and of no account or value, was hollow and filled with gold.

When the three young men came out of the sacred precincts, Brutus the dullard pretended to stumble, and fell upon his hands and knees, and thereby he kissed the earth. Looking upon his two companions, he said: "The earth is the true mother of us all."

III

When the three men returned to Rome, King Tarquin was in camp with the army against the people of Ardea. The city was strong and the siege was long and leisurely. The King, said the people of Rome, only wished to win more spoils to pay for more spectacular buildings!

Had Tarquin, however, been in the city, he would have been surprised to learn how Brutus, since his return from Delphi, was using every opportunity to foster discontent among the people. To the patricians, who snubbed him for being declassed, Brutus was scornfully preaching submission to the tyrant, lest they should be reduced in rank as he had been. To the senators he pretended to apologize that he, a plebeian, should be forced into their august body as commander of the decurions, and deprecated that both the ancient Ramnes and the Quirites should be forced to bow to a foreign king. But with the plebeians he mourned over the discarded laws of Servius; and with the laborers and the slaves he lamented that their work should be so heavy and their pay so small.

Tarquin's sons, Lucius, Sextus and Aruns, were in camp with the King. The war was flagging, and the princes, with the most brilliant officers, were spending their time in sports and hunting. One day they tried stag hunting in the Etruscan fashion. It was a somewhat extraordinary way of hunting, for instead of using dogs and nets they hunted the stag with music. Of course, the nets were spread in the customary way; but when all was ready, a flute played a melodious tune. In the calm and silence of the forest the notes of the flute expanded in an uncanny way, unfolding their plaintive call down to the ponds and groves where the herds were grazing. And when the music reached their ears, the stags came forth and stood bewitched, while the huntsmen drew the nets and slew them.

In the evening, after the hunt, the three princes were supping in their tent with their cousin Collatinus, and the conversation turned upon the merit and virtues of their respective wives. The topic was a testy one; and the four young men agreed to ride first to Rome and then to Collatia and decide the point by a surprise visit to their wives.

They mounted their horses, escorted by some officers, and galloped the few miles to Rome. The Tarquin princesses were feasting at the palace in company with their ladies; they had no reason to do otherwise.

Then the party rode on to Collatia. By then the evening had turned into night; but the beautiful Lady Lucrece, wife of Governor Collatinus, was still sitting with her handmaiden working at the loom.

"Domus manuit, lanam fecit!" joyously and proudly cried Collatinus. Among laughter and drinks the four men toasted the virtuous Lucrece as the most worthy wife. Lucrece dutifully entertained her husband and kinsmen; and afterward they rode back to camp.

Lucrece's simple manners were styled on the rules of the matrons of earlier times. They were, in fact, an ostentation, a challenge to the freer and looser manners and habits of the ladies in the luxurious palace of the Tarquinian princes.

The palace was full of ostentatious refinement, with its rich Etruscan furniture and works of art, and an abundance of slaves who worked as servants, cooks, domestics and even as permanent musicians, dancers and athletes to amuse the company at dinner. Lucrece's house was comfortable but plain, almost severe-looking in its simplicity, like Lucrece's dress and demeanor and her insistence on traditional rules and customs. One would have said that the prim and proud Lady Lucrece wore her modesty like a political badge.

But the virtuous wife of Collatinus was a very beautiful woman. She was tall and well built and had auburn hair, which was rare in Rome, as rare was her milk-white complexion. Her eyes, gray and calm, added charm to her serious face.

Sextus Tarquinius had been fascinated by that face; his eyes had roved lustfully over her body, greedily watching the bosom heaving under the simple peplum, the generous hips speaking of a deep warm lap.

The sight of the beautiful Lucrece inflamed Sextus' passions. An overwhelming desire possessed this son of Tarquin. Unable to restrain his lust, the following night he came back to Collatia alone and presented himself at Collatinus' house on some slender pretext. Lucrece received him with the courtesy due the King's son and gave him hospitality.

In the dead of night, Sextus left his bed, madly tossed between desire and dread. He entered Lucrece's room and with choking voice told her that if she did not submit to him he would murder her and then kill a slave by her side. The world would believe his story that he had done it to avenge the honor of her husband.

The rape accomplished, Sextus went back to the camp.

The proud Lucrece "woke up her heart by beating on her breast"; and at dawn she sent a messenger to her father in Rome and also one to her husband in camp, bidding them to come instantly, for a dreadful thing had happened in her house.

Her father, Lucretius, who was acting as the King's lieutenant in Rome, brought with him Publius Valerius and Lucius Brutus.

When the four men stood before her, Lucrece told them unflinchingly the offense that she had been subjected to. "But ere I name him, you fair lords shall plight your honorable faiths to me, with swift pursuit to venge this wrong of mine." And uttering Sextus' name: "I am not guilty," she said, "yet must I too share in the punishment of this deed," [1] and drawing a dagger from the folds of her dress she stabbed herself to the heart.

Stone-still stood her husband, Collatinus, and her father, Lucretius. But Brutus swiftly drew the knife from the wound, held it up, and with all his long-pent hatred and burning passion, cried: "By this blood which was so pure before the misdeed, and was defiled by the outrage of the King's son; by you, O immortal Gods, I swear that I will follow as far as Avernum Tarquin the Proud and his abominable wife and all his criminal progeny, and will not tolerate that they nor any man hereafter shall be King in Rome!"

Brutus kissed the fatal steel, and passed it to the father, to the husband and to Valerius; and all three, stupefied as though in the presence of a prodigy by this sudden outburst from Brutus, repeated the oath to avenge Lucrece's death and to free themselves of the hated yoke that bound Rome down.

The four men ordered that the body of Lucrece should be immediately carried to Rome and deposited in the forum. On learning the news, the people of Collatia were deeply moved. The men took up arms and set guards at the gates that none might go out to carry the tidings to King Tarquin in his camp at Ardea. Then a great number of people followed Lucius Brutus and the procession of mourners to Rome.

The Romans at first shut their gates, not knowing what to make of the warlike procession. But when they saw Brutus and Lucretius at the head of it, all the people came forward, and the criers summoned them to assemble before the tribune of the celeres in the forum.

---

[1] Shakespeare, *The Rape of Lucrece.*

Standing by the bier, Brutus told the assembled people the dreadful tale, over the exposed body of Lucrece. "Behold the deeds of the wicked family of the Tarquins! O immortal Gods," cried Brutus with all the glow of hatred, "do I need retell the story? I still hear in my mind the cries of good King Servius slain by his son-in-law. I see his horrid and impious daughter, trailing the corpse of her father tied to the hoofs of the mad horses.

"O Furies of unnatural children, their hour has come; make haste and clean our walls! And as a throne makes a king forget so soon that it is the people that gives it, O Romans! let us crush the throne and give freedom to the people!"

The voice of the plebs sounded the call to arms: "For liberty, and death to the tyrant!"

The representatives of the curiae announced that all sovereign power was henceforth taken back from Tarquin and that the King and all his family were banished from Rome.

All night the cries of revolt and of war resounded in Rome. Lucius Brutus was acclaimed the people's leader.

That same night, King Tarquin's wife, the wreched Tullia, now old and feeble but yet undaunted and haughty, the Queen who had mitigated no evil in her husband's rule, took flight from Rome, while all cursed her as she passed, calling upon her the Furies of her father's blood.

The following day Lucrece's funeral was attended with great solemnity and ritual. The body was exhibited outside her parental house and all citizens came to pay their last salutations. Then, at sunset, the bier was carried into the forum upon a magnificent hearse. On the lofty catafalque Lucrece's body was a dignified figure, and her face was serene in death, standing out on the headrest, her white matronly robe marked on the left side by a deep stain, to remind the onlookers of her self-inflicted noble death. Before the catafalque marched the train of ancestors, impersonated by actors—generals, praetors, high officers of state. Above each a card declared his identity. Behind the bier walked her grieving husband and father.

The procession reached the forum. It halted by the speakers' tribune; and Brutus mounted it. By the time his speech had ended the crowd was in great turmoil.

On the Campus Martius an immense pyre had been erected. Built like a pyramid, it was draped with purple-edged hangings and adorned with images celebrating the virtues of womanhood. About the stages of the pyre were distributed the offerings from the senate and the populace: gifts of food, clothing, ornaments, statuettes of wax that would melt in the flames and keep the evil spirits away, and all those things which might please the dead Lucrece or be of use in the nether world. The pyre was sprayed with sweet-smelling spices, incense and balms.

All around, thousands of people clustered thick on the roofs of the surrounding buildings and porticoes, and grandstands had been hastily erected for dignitaries and senators. All the patricians who were not in camp were present, many of them wondering what this exceptional funeral might portend.

The procession drew nearer and marched around. The spectators rose to their feet, and each man and woman extended the right arm and greeted the dead Lucrece with the flat of the hand. The procession reached the pyre, and the bier was carried to the top and set down. Collatinus opened the eyes of the dead Lucrece and kissed her; and so did her father Lucretius. Together they stood beside the bier while down below a long line of matrons and virgins filed past and a band of flutes played mournful tunes. Then they descended, and with averted faces kindled the fire.

When the tongues of flames darted upward, a white dove and an eagle rose into the air from the very top of the pyre.

In a few minutes the pyre was a mass of flames. The burning perfumes gave out a strong, stupefying odor. The onlookers, however, deterred neither by the heat nor by the reeking fumes, pressed up to the pyre and shouted, "Farewell, Lucrece, farewell, O noble and proud Lucrece!" And they cast their last gifts into the flames—garlands, clothes, locks of hair, jewels.

And suddenly a voice was heard—the shrieking voice of Brutus: "Be your death the avenger of Roman freedom, O Lucrece! Out from your pyre the eagle of Rome has risen to tell the gods that the Roman people shall be free!"

At this a rush of hysteria swept over the mass of the people, some genuine, and some pretended enthusiasm. The crowd clamored aloud, the horns and trumpets sounded; the eagle could still be seen beating up into the sky. And here and there raucous voices were calling out: "Brutus, O Brutus, the avenger of the people!"

The pyre burned down very quickly. The glowing embers were quenched with wine. At last the bones were collected, washed in milk, dried with a linen cloth and laid with salves and spices into an urn. Later the family carried the urn to the cemetery outside the city and deposited it in their tomb.

The smoke of the pyre seemed to remain all night like a pall over the plebeian districts, and the name of Brutus resounded throughout the night.

The death of Lucrece became instantly a myth; and it was of no use for some to murmur that Lucrece had killed herself merely because she felt she was an adulteress, and in her virtue she could not stand so great a shame. "Why"—some said—"why did she not slay Tarquin's son? She sacrificed her life to her honor, yet had she kept her mind unconquered, she would have lived the mirror of women; but her weakness pressed her down to die in her despair, rather than live after she was dishonored."

But there are deeds that seize the imagination of men, and no force of reasoning can dim their brightness. The episode of Lucrece appeared to the people of Rome as though it had been ordained by the gods, and it entered the realm of legend.[1]

---

1 The date is traditionally given as 509 B.C.

BOOK FIVE

———————

THE

VENGEANCE

OF

BRUTUS

I

King Tarquin heard the news in camp and was at first disinclined to believe it. To his counselors he expressed the opinion that it was a misfortune that his fool of a son Sextus should hit upon a woman belonging to one of the most powerful families instead of choosing an ordinary wench.[1] Then he set out with all speed to Rome to quell the tumult.

But Tarquin completely misjudged the real character of Brutus. Lucius Brutus by-passed the small forces that the King had taken with him; he came to the camp near Ardea and the Roman soldiers received him as the savior of the people.

When Tarquin reached Rome, he found the gates closed. The troops in the city refused to obey the King's call, and from the city walls the representatives of the plebs read to the King the sentence of banishment which had been passed against him and his family.

The army in camp below Ardea was composed of Romans, Latins and Etruscans, for Tarquin was the King of Rome, the chosen leader of all Latium and a member of the great Etruscan League. The Roman legions and most of his Latin

---

[1] Cicero.

cohorts deserted him. Only the Tuscans remained loyal to Tarquin and with them he retired to Caere with his wife, Tullia, and his sons Lucius and Aruns. There he decided to wait until the Romans returned to their senses.

Some days later, Tarquin decided to send ambassadors to Rome, and this was a serious mistake. The King was counting on the many friends he had in the city, and he thought that once the excitement over the funeral of Lucrece was over and the fury of the people was spent, things would return to normal.

But soon he received the news that his son Sextus, seeking refuge in his official residence at Gabii, had been killed by the people there, who had not forgotten how he had betrayed them to his father. The really puzzling point to Tarquin was why Collatinus had not avenged the affront in person. Perhaps his Etruscan blood prevented him from vindicating his honor by killing a kinsman, or maybe supineness and feebleness [1] had prevented him.

In Rome Tarquin's ambassadors were honorably received. The purpose of the embassy was dual—to submit, in the first place, that King Tarquin could not be considered a party to the iniquity of his son Sextus. If this appeal failed and if the Roman people were determined to end the monarchy, the ambassadors were to demand that the King's property should be valued and the equivalent given to him.

Secretly, the ambassadors were to negotiate a loan to bribe the most influential senators to have the King restored.

The ambassadors went, very discreetly, to the sunny side of the forum where the argentarii had their banks; but the proposal did not work. The bankers might have been prepared to consider the proposition against adequate securities, but the Tarquinian partisans were too frightened to accept bribes. There was in the air an atmosphere of repression, and Brutus was speaking of a "purge" of the senatorial ranks.

---

1 Livy, I, 60.

Brutus laughed at the King's demands for reparation. Brutus had attained his object; he had driven away the Tarquinian dynasty that had declassed his father and made him a plebeian. A man of the plebs he was now, and the people had placed him in the King's place. There is no more rabid revolutionary than the man who, for personal vengeance, speaks in the name of liberty.

Besides, the King's ambassadors found the city in most unexpected order. There was a regular government of which Brutus was at the head, with all the apparel of kingly pomp. The vociferous demogogue had said: "Let us follow once more the just laws of good King Servius; let us meet in our centuries, according as he directed, and let us choose two men year by year to govern us instead of a king."

Such portions of the laws of Servius as had escaped destruction were consulted. The centuries met in the Field of Mars.

Spurius Lucretius, father of Lucrece, was appointed custos urbis, or interrex; and he called the senate and the curiae to decide upon their rulers and the centuries to give their consent. The supreme authority was divided between patricians and plebeians, and two men were chosen to rule Lucius Junius Brutus and Lucius Collatinus, the bereaved husband of Lucrece.

The senate decided to preserve the name of Rex for the consuls and the other sacred officer who was, since ancient times, called Rex Sacrorum and his person was inviolable. This officer was henceforth to be chosen by the augurs and the pontifices, and he would never meddle in civil affairs. His wife was Regina and chief priestess. None but a patrician could enjoy this dignity, and the Rex Sacrorum had to be a man educated in Etruria and versed in all science of the religious disciplina. But he was now to be subject to the Roman consuls.

The first inconsistency of democratic rule was that the two consuls were entitled to wear the golden crown, the royal purple robe, to hold in their hands the ivory scepter and be preceded by the lictors carrying the fasces. Brutus saw the

flaw in this; and lest there should seem to be two kings instead of one, he made the centuries decide that only one of
the two consuls should rule at one time and the lictors should
walk with their rods before him alone. The two consuls
would rule alternatively month by month.

Many members of the old families were of the opinion that
King Tarquin's exile ought to be rendered as light as possible, and that to begin with, his property should be returned.
Some of the old families went so far as to leave the city to join
the King.

The stubborn attitude of Brutus gave rise to a monarchist
plot. Tarquin's ambassadors had succeeded in corrupting
two of the best families in Rome, the Aquilii, in which were
three senators, and the Vitellii, among whom were two. All
these, on their mother's side, were nephews of Collatinus the
consul. The Vitellii were also related to Brutus, for their sis-
ter was his wife; and the Vitellii drew into the conspiracy
two of Brutus' own sons, Titus and Tiberius. The two young
men were persuaded by the prospect of perhaps marrying
into the family of the Tarquins, of sharing in their royal
fortunes and being set free from the yoke of a stupid and
cruel father.

The two sons of Brutus were brought to confer with the
Aquilii, and all agreed to take a great and terrible oath,
sealed by drinking the blood and eating of the entrails of a
man sacrificed for that purpose. This ceremony was performed in the house of the Aquilii, in a darkened room. The
drinking of blood was meant to bind every member of the
conspiracy to inviolable secrecy.

But a slave named Vindicius lurked there, hiding behind
a chest. He overheard the terrible vow that they were to kill
the consuls, and wrote to Tarquin informing him of their
intentions. The letters were entrusted to the ambassadors
who were guests of the Aquilii.

The slave Vindicius hesitated to go to Brutus with this
accusation of evil intent against Brutus by his own sons.

Finally he went for advice to the great public man Valerius, who had, out of respect, surrendered his place as consul to Collatinus. Valerius heard the slave Vindicius in the presence of his brother Marcus and his wife. Astonished and terrified at the plot, he would not let the man go, but shut him up in the room and set his wife to watch the door. Then he ordered his brother Marcus to surround the late King's palace, to seize the letters if possible and to secure the servants, while he himself, with the friends whom he always had about him and a retinue of servants, went to the house of the Aquilii. The Aquilii were not there but he forced his way in and found the letters in the ambassadors' room. On hearing of the search, the Aquilii ran home and engaged Valerius at the door, endeavoring to retrieve the letters. But Valerius and his party repelled the attack, and after much struggling dragged the Aquilii into the forum. Marcus Valerius had the same success at the royal palace, where he seized other letters.

When the consuls had put a stop to this tumult, Valerius produced the slave Vindicius, and the accusation was lodged and the letters were read.

A dramatic silence fell upon the crowd, and some, out of pity for Brutus himself, suggested banishment of the conspirators. The tears of Collatinus and the silence of Valerius gave hopes of mercy. But Brutus called each of his sons by name, and said: "You Titus, and you Tiberius, why do you not make your defense against the charge?" After they had thus been questioned three times and made no answer, Brutus turned to the lictors and said: "Do your part."

The lictors immediately laid hold of the youths, stripped them of their garments, tied their hands behind them, and flogged them mercilessly with their rods. And though others turned their eyes aside, unable to endure the spectacle, Brutus neither looked away nor let pity in the least soften his stern and angry countenance. He watched while his sons were pinioned on the ground and the lictors cut their heads off with axes.

Then he departed, leaving the rest to his colleague.[1] Some of the watching crowd marveled at him, and sycophants shouted that this showed how Junius Brutus loved justice and freedom much more than his own flesh and blood, and that it would be an example that would be retold by men in all lands forever. But the realization of what was done struck horror in others. The forbearance of Collatinus gave hope to the Aquilii to beg time for their defense, and they asked that their slave Vindicius be restored to them. Consul Collatinus was inclined to grant their request and dismiss the assembly, but Valerius would not suffer the traitors to be dismissed. At last he seized the criminals himself and called for Brutus, exclaiming that Collatinus acted most unworthily in laying his colleague under the dire necessity of putting his own sons to death and then in trying to gratify the women relatives by releasing the enemies of their country. Collatinus commanded Vindicius to be taken away, the friends of Valerius stood upon their defense, and the people cried out for Brutus.

Brutus returned, but said that it was enough for him to give judgment upon his own sons, and for the rest he left them to the sentence of the people, who were now free.

Immediately the crowd put the sentence of the Aquilii to vote, and with one voice they condemned them to die, so the conspirators were beheaded. At Valerius' request the slave Vindicius was declared a freedman, with the full rights of citizenship, which had never been conferred on a slave before. The act of enfranchising a slave was ever after called vindicta, from Vindicius.

The attitude of Collatinus in this grave matter of the conspirators made the crowd suspect him, on account of his near relationship with the Tarquinian family. Brutus considered him a hindrance to his plans. To Collatinus privately he hinted at the certainty of an immediate rupture with Tar-

---

[1] Livy, II, 5. "*Quum inter omne tempus pater, Vultusque, et os ejus spectaculo esset; eminente animo patrio inter publicae penae ministerium.*"

Also Virgil, in the *Aeneid*, exalts Brutus for this episode, but does not hesitate to attribute it to a base love of popular applause: "*Vincit amor patriae, laudumque immensa cupido.*"

quinia and the embarrassing position he would be in of
fighting his own kin. Collatinus was a mild man, and knowing well the irascibility of Brutus' temper, he took up his
franchise and retired to Lavinium, beyond the jurisdiction of
Rome. Thus the man whose proud honor had been the cause
of installing the republic in Rome, and who had been elected
one of the two first democratic rulers of the people, was
forced by his colleague to disappear from the political scene.

Having thus rid himself of Collatinus, Lucius Brutus had
Publius Valerius elected to rule with him. The people declared Valerius Consul with great honor, as a mark of gratitude for his patriotic zeal. Many more of the laws of King
Servius were restored. The people again chose their judges to
try all cases between a man and his neighbor.

At that time ambassadors came from Carthage to conclude
with the new government of Rome a treaty of peace and commerce. In this treaty Rome was permitted to trade with Sardinia, Corsica, Sicily and with the whole of North Africa
from the Bay of Carthage as far as the Pillars of Hercules or
Straits of Gibraltar. Rome, however, undertook not to interfere with the trade of Egypt; and, on these conditions,
Carthage promised to respect the trade of Ardea, Antium,
Circeii, Terracina and Aricia, and to make no conquests and
build no forts in those small states even should they cease to
be dependencies of Rome. The treaty was engraved upon
stone in the forum and also upon tables of brass to be kept in
the Capitol.

This important treaty with Carthage was a great blow to
Tarquin's cause, for it acknowledged the authority of the new
government in Rome. His ambassadors found that his restoration was by now out of the question; but they still lingered
in Rome pleading the return of the ex-King's property. After
a while, the senate decreed that Tarquin's properties should
be given back. But Brutus was determined that Tarquin's
riches should not leave Rome, and he opposed the senate's

decision, asserting that he was sure they would be used against the city.

The next step taken by Brutus was to give the houses and properties of King Tarquin to be plundered by the people.

The palace and other houses were leveled to the ground. The pleasantest part of the Campus Martius had been in the royal family's possession, and this was now consecrated to the god Mars. It happened to be the time of harvest, and the sheaves lay upon the ground. But as the ground was now consecrated it would not be lawful to thresh the corn; a great number of people, therefore, took it up in baskets and threw it into the river. The trees were also cut down and thrown in after the corn, and the ground was left entirely without fruit or crop, never to be tilled again. A great quantity of other possessions of the royal family was also thrown into the river, too many for the current to carry them beyond the shallows where the first heaps had accumulated. Finding no further passage, everything piled up there, in the river mud which acted as a cement. Thus gradually the debris of what had been King Tarquin's palace and all his goods became the island Tiberina, and in time the Romans built upon it several temples and porticoes.

II

The execution of Brutus' two sons proved the deciding turn of the revolution. Who in Rome would dare, after the death of the Consul's own children, to think of Tarquin's return?

When King Tarquin found that the plot had failed and his properties were plundered and destroyed, he turned for help to Tarquinia and Veii. An army was assembled, and Tarquin led them against Rome.

Aruns, Tarquin's son, commanded the cavalry; Tarquin followed with the legions. When they entered the Roman territories, the consuls marched to meet them—Valerius led the infantry and Brutus was at the head of the cavalry. Aruns, seeing Brutus with the kingly purple over his shoulders and Tarquin's crown upon his helmet, surrounded by the lictors like a king, cried out: "There is the villain who has banished us from our native country! See how he rides in state! Now assist me, Gods, avenger of Kings!" He leveled his spear and furiously spurred his horse against him. Brutus met him head-on and each ran his spear through the other. Both were killed instantly.

The battle went on desperately. Two of the sons of Tarquin who commanded the left wing of the Etruscans defeated the right wing of the Romans and were on the point of forcing the issue, but at nightfall the battle was still undecided. Eleven thousand two hundred and ninety-nine of the Romans and eleven thousand three hundred of the Veientines were left dead upon the field.

But in the night there came out of the Arsian forest a voice that said: "One more has fallen on the side of the Etruscans than on the Romans. Rome is victorious in this war."

At this the Etruscans were afraid, and believing the voice, they immediately marched home to their own cities, while the Romans collected the spoils and returned in triumph to Rome. With them they took the dead body of Brutus.

The public grief turned Brutus' funeral into his triumph. The most illustrious officers took the hero's corpse and brought it to Rome covered with palms and flowers. The entire army paid tribute; the whole senate went to meet the bier outside the walls. Consul Valerius in mourning garb placed the bier between the trophies in the forum, and mounting the rostrum he extolled the good fortune of Brutus, who "after delivering his country had died vested with the supreme power, fighting bravely, when his glory was at its height."

One year's public mourning was ordered, as for the father of all citizens, and all the matrons mourned him well because he had avenged Lucrece.

Thus Brutus passed away; and his name remained forever engraved upon the Roman people's memory because poetry attributed to him high motives which he never owned. For Brutus' own ideas of liberty were inconsistent with his supreme command. This command he had craved as a vengeance for the offense inflicted upon his father and upon himself by King Tarquin, and he had purchased it, as it were, from the Oracle at Delphi. He called himself Rex, and he died with the kingly purple over his shoulders. Yet the Romans honored and revered him as the hero who had placed the government into the hands of the people. And ever after the Romans did not look upon it as so glorious a work for

Romulus to have built the city as for Brutus to have founded and established the republic. A statue of brass was erected to him and placed in the Capitol amongst the kings.

After the battle in which Brutus fell, the Romans were content to keep to their own territory, and they made a truce with Veii. Publius Valerius was allowed to govern by himself, and he was a popular and moderate man. He began to build himself a new house, a great strong house on the Velium Hill, which looked down upon the forum. But some began to murmur. "Brutus," they said, "who was the father of liberty, would not rule alone, but took to himself a first and second colleague; yet this man Publius is grasping the whole authority, and is not the successor to the Consulate of Brutus but to the tyranny of Tarquin. To what purpose is it in words to extol Brutus in his funeral oration, and in deeds to imitate Tarquin, and have all the rods and axes carried before him alone, and set out from a house more stately than the royal palace which he demolished? Publius wants to live like a king and is building for himself a house that is like a citadel."

When he heard of this, Publius called a meeting of the people, and he went among the crowd and ordered his lictors who walked before him to lower the fasces to show that he considered the people to be greater than himself. It was a most gratifying sight for the crowd to be shown that the majesty and power of the people were greater than that of the consul. Then Valerius said that the people had mistrusted him, and he had no intention of building his house on the top of the Velium but at the bottom of the hill, and his house would not be a stronghold. He promptly called on the people to make a law that whoever tried to make himself king should be accursed and anyone would be right in slaying him. Also, that the people should have a right of appeal against a magistrate.

So much pleased were the plebs by these laws that all said that Publius was a true lover of the people, and he was surnamed Publicola, which from that day came to mean "the people's friend."

During this time, the people hoped to propitiate the gods by completing the great temple of Jupiter Capitolinus; and they looked upon it as a happy omen that King Tarquin, albeit he did consecrate it, had not left it perfectly finished.

The Aediles, therefore, asked the Veii manufacturers to deliver the chariot and horses of terracotta which they had been ordered to make for the pediment of the temple. But a strange thing occurred while the potters were getting the equestrian group out of the kiln. The clay, instead of shrinking in the fire, had swelled to a very unusual size, and the workmen considered this a portent about which the augurs must be consulted, the more so as the chariot could not be withdrawn from the kiln without breaking the furnace.

The augurs answered that this chariot betokened power and success; and the Veientines determined not to give it up to the Romans, and when the Romans, irritated by the delay, finally sent for it, the Veientines told them that the chariot had been commissioned by King Tarquin and they would deliver it to the King but not to those who had driven the King from his kingdom.

The position was somewhat embarrassing, for Rome had just made a treaty of peace with the city of Veii. But it happened that a few days later the great Circensian games of Veii were being celebrated, and a man named Ratumena received the prize for the chariot race, and as he was leading his horses out of the ring the animals inexplicably took fright and bolted down the hill and through the gates of the city. They careered along the road and across the frontier, and never stopped until they reached the gates of Rome, where at the sudden halt Ratumena was flung out and killed.

No sign from heaven could be clearer: the Romans at once renamed this gate "Ratumena"; and the people of Veii, fearing the gods' wrath, delivered the equestrian group. The splendid chariot was then placed in triumph upon the front of Jupiter's temple on the Capitol.

Thus was the great temple completed, and Consul Publius Valerius drew lots with his colleague Marcus Horatius, who had been elected consul with Publicola, as to who should dedicate the temple. The lot fell to Marcus, to the great disappointment of the friends of the popular Publicola. So that when Marcus Horatius was about to open the ceremony, and had his hand on the doorpost of the temple and was speaking the words of invocation, the brother of Publicola came running up the one hundred broad steps, and with halting words cried out: "Consul, your son lies dead in the camp." "Let them carry him out and bury him," answered Marcus Horatius, "I admit no mourning on this occasion," and without a tear or a word of lament he struck in the nail of the new lustrum.[1]

---

[1] Livy, VII, 3.

III

It was now many months since Lars Porsenna had brought his huge army from the height of Clusium to lay siege to Rome; and Porsenna had marched against Rome to help King Tarquin to regain his throne. On the city walls—the walls that Tarquinius Priscus had built, with the masonry along the Tiber no less colossal than the works of Babylon along the banks of the Euphrates—the guards walked grimly from post to post.

Rome was defended on all sides. First there was a moat, then a rampart of grass and lastly the walls, thirty cubits high, built of bricks and of cut stone, and presenting two stages. On the city side the walls contained, or abutted, the stables of the cavalry, with storerooms for their vestments and armor and food. Moreover, at suitable intervals along the walls and in the vicinity of the city gates, there were the barracks for the one hundred thousand troops who formed the Roman army. Each barracks had muniment rooms for the artillery, onagers (catapults), ballistas and other war engines. Along the second or upper wall, at regular intervals, rose towers with crenelated tops and holes for archers. Outside were huge shields of bronze affixed to hooks.

Within this girdle of walls and ramparts one could see the

higher districts of the city crowding the summits of the seven
hills: only the Capitol was clear of houses and streets, as it
was the holy precinct of the temple of Jupiter.

The houses, mostly of dark-red bricks, a few only of stone,
were not very high, and were covered with tiled roofs. One
could not see the principal and official buildings, as they stood
on the plain at the foot of the hills; but the groves of the
temples stood out as pleasant oases of verdure against the red
background of the houses.

From afar, where the ground rose again in the gentle hills
among which ran the main road to Etruria, the enemy army
could recognize the districts of the city, the temples with their
columns, and the metopes painted in gay colors or decorated
with the statuary manufactured in Veii. At the foot of the
Capitol and all along the Velabrum, the river banks were
crowded with ships, now inactive and prevented from carrying and unloading provisions and food for the city. One could
see the idle markets, filled with a milling throng of resentful
and agitated gossipers.

When Tarquin had found that the aid of Caere, Veii and
Tarquinia herself was not sufficient to beat the rebellious
Romans, now reinforced by the people of Antium and Circeii
and their other Latin allies, he had gone as a suppliant to
Porsenna, King of Clusium, who was acclaimed the bravest
warrior and most magnanimous sovereign: Tarquin had submitted his case to Lars Porsenna and begged his mighty
support against the democratic upstarts of Rome.

Tarquin had journeyed three days, following the road from
Viterbo to Clusium; and he had traveled in great style, to
make a good impression on King Porsenna.

Clusium stood on top of the hills, exactly where Etruria
joined with Umbria. The landscape was beautiful, almost
poetically so, and at the same time most suited to defense, all
hills and narrow valleys: King Porsenna's palace rose at the
very top of the steep ascent that led to the city, and from its
terraces the eye rested on the Lake of Clusium, a turquoise
gem in the verdant cup of the opening valleys.

There was a deep irony in Tarquin's situation. For even if Prince Sextus had not been a villain, incapable of controlling his lust, nor Lucius Junius Brutus an ambitious avenger of the wrongs suffered by his family, and had old King Tarquin remained free from violence in Rome, Tarquin would, in any case, have ended his days in strife and warfare. He would have had to defend himself against that very great Lars Porsenna, at the foot of whose throne he was now glad to seek shelter as a suppliant. At the very time of the absurd incident of the rape of Lucrece, Tarquin was busily engaged in warlike operations, and in his secret heart he burned with hostile feelings against his great northern rival of Clusium, who, ruling the state that was the political competitor of Tarquinia, was automatically the opponent of the aristocratic party which looked to Tarquin as its head.

Why then did Porsenna agree to assist Tarquin and his Tarquinian party in Rome, if he was so clearly opposed to their interests in the Etruscan League? Porsenna was a subtle king. He was, indeed, opposed to King Tarquin and his party, yet the object of the upstart Brutus and of the present republican faction in Rome was, quite clearly, to emancipate Rome from Etruscan influence. And although Porsenna was determined to pursue the cause of Clusium against the preponderance of Tarquinia and of Tarquin's dynasty, he was not prepared to suffer the Etruscan influence to be destroyed in the great border city on the banks of the Tiber, or Rome to become not only free from kingly rule but from Etruscan domination. For, though Lars Porsenna might be an enemy of the Tarquinians, he was an Etruscan, a descendant of the mighty Tyrrheni, worthy to have lived in the days of the demigods, and as such he was always prepared to turn his powerful forces against other enemies of Etruria.

When he saw King Tarquin, so venerable and aged, so renowned for his magnificent works and so valiant in war, supplicating his aid, Porsenna relented and resolved to give his succor and march against Rome. In his opinion, Tarquin had been harshly and unjustly used, and he did not understand a plebeian rebel lording over the patricians and appointing himself to the supreme authority: if King Tarquin was to suffer for the misdeed of his son, by the same token Lucius Brutus, whose life and property Tarquin had spared, ought to have suffered long ago for the treason of his own father. Brutus, in Porsenna's opinion, should have been the last man to raise his hand against old King Tarquin; Porsenna was roused to the strongest indignation.

At the general diet of Voltumna, Porsenna had himself elected embratur of the Etruscan League, and assumed the supreme command of the League's army against Rome.

IV

East and west and south and north
The messengers ride fast,
And tower and town and cottage
Have heard the trumpet's blast.
Shame on the false Etruscan
Who lingers in his home,
When Porsena of Clusium
Is on the march for Rome.

—MACAULAY, *Lays of Ancient Rome*

From Volaterrae, "piled by the hands of giants," from sea-girt Populonia "whose sentinels descry Sardinia's snowy mountain ridge, fringing the southern sky," from the proud markets of Pisa, "queen of the western waves, where ride Massilias' triremes, heavy with fair-haired slaves," from Corton lifting to heaven her diadem of towers, from the Ciminian hills, from the Clitumnus' streams, from Arretium, from Umbria, from Luna land of marble and luscious vines, from all the lucumonies of Etruria came the armies to join Lars Porsenna. The great army assembled at Sutrium, and after storming the Janiculum set a siege to Rome.

The augur, who was with the host, chose the ground for the

encampment, marking with his staff the center of the prae-
torium, that was the commander's tent and the heart and
mind of the camp.

Then the fecial came under the wall of the city; covered his
head with a woolen fillet,[1] and cried out: "Hear me, O Jupiter, hear me, you frontiers; let justice hear! I am the author-
ized herald of the Etruscan nations: I come with the forms of
justice and piety. Let faith be given to my words, and Jupiter
be my witness. I require that justice be rendered to King
Tarquin and that the men who did him wrong should be
given up to me."

Thus having spoken, the fecial took an iron spear, burnt at
the point and dipped in blood, and said: "Because this populus and nation have behaved ill to us and our nations,
therefore we conceive war to be just against them, and for
this reason I and my nations declare war against the plebs and
the populus who refuse us justice." Saying this, the fecial
threw the spear against the Roman Gate.

From the walls the Romans could now see the Etruscan
soldiers moving about their camp. The enemy had plentiful
supplies and the Etruscan soldiery seemed to treat the siege
as a holiday. The soldiers walked about without full armor,
discarding the jerkins that were part of their uniform and, in
battle, left their arms and legs completely free. Some wore a
casque of bronze with a crest or comb, others a helmet of the
type called "salad basket," and others again wore a Corinthian helmet proudly adorned with a spray of colored plumes.
Others went about without headgear at all, letting their long
hair flow loosely.

Now and then the Romans heard the notes of the tubae,
and the troops would run from all sides and fall in, in battle
formation; but the Etruscans were only drilling. Yet, from
the wall the Roman troops recognized the various armors of
the enemy; the shield, small and round, often decorated with

---

1 Such as we see on many Etruscan statues.

geometric patterns or designs meant to frighten the enemy; and their new type of double-ax, or the lance, the javelin, the sword straight or curved, the short broadsword and the dagger. The Romans knew that the Etruscans were trained to fight in the very same way as themselves, holding the lance in one hand and the dagger in the other.

The enemy did not seem to be in a hurry to make an attack. They sat comfortably in camp and waited.

The Roman commanders asked the senate to requisition all horses and mules and all arms. Some citizens tried to dissimulate their wealth: but the consuls ordered their properties to be sold and confiscated; and to discourage the avarice of others, the consuls presented the victualing center with two thousand bushels of wheat.

The ramparts were reinforced; and to obtain stones many old houses were pulled down. But the difference in private fortunes was still separating the new tribes from the ancient patricians.

The Roman commanders had devised a clever trick of arranging the troops in pairs, all along the columns, one strong man and one weak, alternately, so that the less strong and less valiant was both led and pushed by two others. The number of slingers was increased and set to practice from the ramparts, casting their stones and missiles on the enemy camping below. The cavalry, armored by strips of bronze clipped together, which gave a freer movement to the cavalrymen, was practicing a new technique, which the Roman commander had heard was that followed by the Tarentinians— of using the bow and arrows from the horse, and carrying at the belt, instead of a spear, a double-edged ax.

Yet, Lars Porsenna still sat under his tent, and the siege went on, and Rome began to feel hunger. And the name of Porsenna began to be whispered with terror by the people in the besieged city. Porsenna was ravaging the country; he had captured the Janiculum and lodged some chosen troops inside its fortress.

And now, suddenly, in spite of oracles and prodigies, and

deaf to the plebeian prayers for liberty and grace, Porsenna descended upon the Sublicius Bridge and resolved to cross it into the city.

A great fear spread in Rome at this news. The bridge was an old one, built of wood, and mortised together with timber alone, without iron. It was considered by tradition to be a holy bridge.

A plebeian, Horatius Cocles—so called because he had lost an eye in battle, an old soldier noted for his valor, offered to keep guard on the bridge at all hazard, until the Roman flying column, that had made a sortie, should have time to return into the city. Two others volunteered to support Horatius.

It was a vital effort, for the city had no wall in that section next to the river. The three men succeeded in halting the pursuers, and the Roman troops retreated safely, till only Horatius Cocles was left unaided on the bridge.

From the city the consuls and the rest of the people were now calling to him to retire; but Horatius remained on his spot, and called to his companions Herminius and Lartius to order that the bridge be cut off next to the city; and when the greatest part of the bridge was broken down they should let him know by some signals or by shouting, and he would take care of the rest.

Horatius Cocles was now alone upon the bridge. When an enemy soldier advanced, he struck with his sword and beat down with his shield. Porsenna's men thought he was a madman, and they hesitated to approach him, nor was it easy to come near him, because the river defended him on the right and left, and before him lay a heap of dead bodies. But standing at a distance the Etruscans threw arrows and spears and large stones at him and even hurled their swords and bucklers. Still Horatius fought, throwing back their own weapons as missiles. He was by now wounded in many places, and a wound in the hip, inflicted by a spear, was causing him great pain and impeding his movements.

At last, those behind him called out that the bridge was

severed. Hearing the welcome signal, Horatius prayed aloud: "Tiberine Pater, Te Sancte precor, Haec arma et hunc militem, propitio flumine accipias!" [1] And armed as he was, he leaped into the Tiber, and swimming across the strong stream with difficulty, for the current, divided by the piles, ran swift, and amid showers of darts hurled on him, he landed safely.

King Porsenna saw the heroic deed and heard the beautiful prayer; and being a noble king, admired Horatius' bravery.

In the city, the Roman troops carried Horatius Cocles to the temple of Sethlans and crowned him with oak leaves. All the citizens ran out to catch a sight of him before he died, because it was thought he could not long survive his many wounds. When he had recovered, the people erected in the forum a statue of him fully armed, and gave him as much of the public land as he could plow around in one day with a yoke of oxen; and every man and woman of some wealth, at a time when they were all suffering famine, gave him as much as would feed a person for one day. The contributors numbered more than three hundred thousand. But hampered by his lameness, the brave Horatius Cocles neither obtained the consulship nor any other military command.

The heroism of Horatius Cocles did not save Rome. The Etruscans still lay before the city; Porsenna occupied both banks of the Tiber blockading the city and threatening the Romans with starvation.

A dreadful famine began. So far, Cuma had managed to send some help; but from the moment that the blockade was complete this source of supply was also cut off.

The senate remitted the taxes to the poor and did all they could to keep the populace quiet. Trouble arose in the city. The elders went into council. Was there a way out?

A young patrician offered to go to the Etruscan camp and assassinate King Porsenna. His name was Caius Mucius. He

---

[1] "Oh holy father Tiber, to whom the Romans pray, this soldier's life and these Romans' arms, take thou in charge in thy propitious stream." Livy, II, 10.

could speak Etruscan. Dressed as an Etruscan he would cross the river and enter the enemy camp. By stealth he would rid Rome of a foe whom they could not repel by force. The senate gave assent.

Mucius crossed the river. He knew that it was the pay day for the Etruscan army. Therefore he might easily enter the King's tent with the many who would assemble there. Moreover, large numbers of slaves had deserted from Rome to the enemy's camp; a stranger would not find admittance difficult.

Mucius had never seen Porsenna, but he stationed himself among the crowd, near the King's tribunal. He saw on a raised seat a very richly dressed officer who was busy paying the troops. This, he thought, must be the King.

He approached, drew his dagger, and stabbed the man to the heart. He happened to be the King's paymaster. Mucius was immediately seized and brought before Porsenna, who was near his domestic altar. The guards threatened Mucius with torture if he did not reveal who had sent him. An incense brazier was burning upon the altar. Mucius thrust his right hand into the fire, saying: "Behold, of how little account bodily pain is to those who have great glory in view." [1]

Porsenna marveled at his courage, and watched the youth let his hand be burned. "Go thy way," the King told him, "for thou hast harmed thyself more than me. I would encourage thee to persevere in thy valor, if that valor stood on the side of my country. I send thee back to Rome unhurt and free."

But Mucius answered: "Since bravery is honored by you, so that you have obtained by kindness what you could not by threats, I warn you that three hundred of us, the flower of Roman youth, have bound themselves to take your life. It was my lot first. Therefore guard yourself well."

Out of gratitude, however, he advised Porsenna to make peace with Rome, whose youths preferred to become assassins rather than yield to a foreign oppressor. Caius Mucius was

---

[1] Livy, II, 12.

henceforth surnamed Scaevola because, having burned his
right hand, he became left-handed.

Porsenna did not follow Mucius' advice to make peace with
Rome. Instead, he destroyed the Roman navy and brought
the ships of Tarquinia and Caere into the Tiber, thus cutting
off the supply by sea. Only then did he request their surrender. Desperate and starving Rome was at last forced to
capitulate.

It was an unconditional surrender—capitulation by "dedi-
tione" [1] into the hands of the great Lars Porsenna. He received
the submission in his tent hung with cloth of gold, his head
crowned with gold, his feet shod in shoes of white kid, his
mantle of precious Tyrian cloth edged with a wide brocaded
border, his chlamys embroidered with male figures in Hellen-
istic style.

"All in heaven and earth—all their temples and sacred
utensils, all their lands and all their houses and all they call
their own" were laid at the feet of Lars Porsenna. By the
ancient laws of Tarchun and of Italy, if he showed the
Romans any mercy, one third of their lands must be forfeited
to the conqueror, and the other two thirds were received back
on payment of tribute and acknowledgment of his sovereignty.

It was total and ignominious capitulation. The Roman
senate ceded the crown and the scepter to Porsenna, and the
robe and the sword which the First Tarquin had received
from Etruria, and the ten Tuscan tribes and the seven Pagi
of Veii disappeared from the map of Rome.

Porsenna made the Romans hand over all their arms and
forbade them to have any iron within their gates except for
purposes of agriculture.

Then and only then did he consent to victual the city, by
ordering their own corn to be sold at public auction "as the
goods of King Porsenna"; and he demanded twenty hostages,

---

[1] Tacitus, III, 72.

ten from the Decem Primi of the original Ramnes families who were the first of the Roman senators, and ten from the Decuriones of the other tribes. He required that the hostages should be not only men, but that women and children should also be included as a pledge that they would keep the peace. Consul Valerius' daughter, Claelia, headed the list of women hostages.

The camp of the Etruscans was near the Tiber, and Claelia, who had courteously been provided with a horse by Porsenna for exercise, escaped with some of her companions and fled to the brink of the river. On being pursued, the girls jumped into the Tiber and swam safely to the other side.

Valerius sent back Claelia and her companions as a sign of good faith. Porsenna declared that Claelia's part in the affair had been greater than the parts played by Cocles and of Scaevola, and bade her to go home free, with any of the other hostages she might choose. Claelia chose those who were of tenderest age. The Romans marked the bravery of Claelia by erecting an equestrian statue at the top of the Via Sacra—a lady sitting on horseback.

Not long afterward Porsenna was recalled home to oppose a timely barrier to the barbarians who were beginning to descend from northern Italy and from beyond the Alps. Before departing from Rome he gave back to the Romans the land which had been won in former times from the Veientines; and also gave them back the Janiculum, and made a present to them of his camp, well-stocked with provisions from the fertile fields of Etruria. His mercy to them was so great and so unexpected that the Romans actually acknowledged him as a hero, and they erected to him a bronze statue in the Comitium, alongside their own seven kings.

On his final return to Clusium, Lars Porsenna built himself an immense and splendid mausoleum, like the tombs of the kings of Egypt, and for a time it was one of the wonders of the world. Each side was 360 feet long and 60 feet high, built of square blocks of stone, and Porsenna made the interior a labyrinth. The structure itself was most singular. Upon the base stood five pyramids: one in the center and four at the corners, each with a base 75 feet square and 150 feet high, tapering to the top, where there was a cupola of bronze. Resting over the five cupolas was a platform of bronze with balls hanging from it on chains, so that they sounded at every breath of wind, like the legendary cauldron of Dodona. And upon this platform of bronze rose four smaller pyramids 100 feet high, and above them, again, rose another story of five pyramids, also of great height. Pliny gives us this account of that strange and colossal structure from a lost work of Varro, who, in the opinion of many ancient writers, actually saw it.

V

Lars Porsenna had not reinstated King Tarquin upon the throne of Rome. And so Tarquin, realizing that he could count no more on Porsenna, left Clusium and went to Tusculum, which was ruled by Octavius Mamilius, who had married Tarquin's daughter.

On the other hand, Rome remained in absolute subjection to Porsenna until his death, and only then was free from the treaty she had made with him. For many years Rome was forced to keep an Etruscan garrison in the city. Porsenna had emancipated Rome altogether from the Tarquinian rule, but he had reduced her once again to the position of the small neutral state that she was at the beginning, for Porsenna believed that in so doing he had re-established the balance of power in Italy.

Now the Consul Publius Valerius was dead, and the people, as evidence of their love, had buried him within the city and the matrons had mourned him for one year; but the example of his republican spirit was spent. The Tarquinian party had once more plenty of supporters in Rome; indeed, ten years after the banishment of the old King, both praetors were strongly in his favor. The people, too, were beginning to say that, all considered, the King was better than the republican rule, and even the slaves and the debtors, at all times a numerous body, showed their sentiment by joining the exiled Romans in an attempt to seize the Capitol.

To stop this unrest, the republic appointed a dictator, Titus Lartius—or Lar Titus—to act against the Tarquinian party, with powers for six months, without any appeal or any responsibility. Titus did his work very well, far more ruthlessly than the exiled Tarquin had. There is a dark episode of nine patricians who were burned at the stake for treason. Publius and Marcus, two former clients of the Tarquinian house, made common cause with the oppressed and the insurgents to seize the Capitol and set fire to the city. The plot was discovered and the ringleaders crucified. Marcus and Publius saved themselves by taking flight; but the following year Marcus and Publius, with a band of debtors—who by now acted as a class—decided to master the ramparts and rush the gates and let in King Tarquin. Paradoxically enough, at this time the Consul Sulpitius was actually negotiating with the Latin cities for the restoration of King Tarquin.

Judging the situation favorable, Octavius Mamilius requested the assistance of the Etruscan cities against Rome. But Etruria thought it wiser to keep the peace and left Tarquin to carry on his cause as best he could. Mamilius, therefore, set in arms his Tusculans, and with the eager body of exiles and some Latins and Volsci, he declared war and marched against Rome with Tarquin.

The Roman senate appointed Aulus Postumius as dictator of the people and Titus Aebutius commander of the cavalry. The whole army was led out to meet the Tarquinian forces in the country of Tusculum. Before the war began, it was resolved that the Latin wives who had married Roman husbands and the Roman wives who had married Latin men were free to leave their husbands if they chose, taking their virgin daughters with them to their countries. All the Latin women except two remained in Rome with their husbands; but the Roman women returned *en masse* to the city of their fathers.

The final battle between Tarquin and Rome took place

at Lake Regillus,[1] and the account is taken from an epic poem.

Tarquin himself was with the army of Mamilius, and so were his surviving sons and all the houses of the Tarquinii. King Tarquin was now far advanced in years, yet he sat his horse and bore his lance as bravely as any of his young officers. He wore a breastplate of gold, chased and embossed to represent Achilles on his war chariot dragging the body of Hector the slayer of his friend Patroclus; and his left arm held an immense shield, with his fist clenched deep in the hollow of this mighty buckler. His greaves were shaped to the calves of his legs. His helmet, upon which he wore his kingly crown, was topped by two figures of men holding by the bridle a horse in war array.

The two armies stood facing one another, and it was a strange sight, for the two phalanxes were almost alike, the Roman army being modeled on the Etruscan. In the front line were the horsemen; then a first line of infantry lightly armed with their tall shields and long spears. Behind them came two lines of heavy infantry. The Romans called the light infantry hastati, and the assault troops were called principes and triarii. On the flanks were ranged the chariots, each guided by a driver, with a soldier at his side holding a long lance.

The troops were distributed in sectors, and at the end of each one could see the cohorts, or velites, and, in the distance, the peculiar helmets of the Clinabares, whose armor shone in the sun, the officers wearing rich breastplates and clusters of plumes upon their crested helmets. Here and there the standards rose high, with brass emblems, from which colored pennants floated in the breeze.

In the middle, compact in its serried ranks, was the phalanx, like a huge cataphract machine. The centurions stood out between long lines of iron, as the six first ranks held their sarissae by the middle, and the next ten ranks held their long lances across the shoulders of the men in front. The faces

---

[1] Now dry, called Labicum or Cornufelle.

of the men were hidden behind the long visors of their helmets, many of which were of Corinthian type, with the sides reaching to the neck, made all of one piece with the crown. The long shields reached below the knees; and this square mass of warriors moved as a solid force.

Above the raucous commands of the officers and centurions rose the notes of the clarions and the sharp whistling of the slings that the men were testing with bullets of lead the size and shape of an almond. The velites, in the rear ranks of the phalanx, held their terrible sickles ready to cut down the legs of the enemy like tall grass in a field.

When the sun was high in the east, King Tarquin rode up to the right of the army. At his side was Octavius Mamilius, who rose on his stirrups and proclaimed to the troops that he would make his father-in-law Tarquin once more King in Rome, and after the victory Tusculum would be the greatest of all the cities whose peoples sacrificed to Jupiter Latial at his temple on the top of the mountain of Alba the Longa.

In front of the Roman army, Aulus Postumius, master of the people, and Titus Aebutius, master of the horsemen, took their position. There was also Titus Herminius, the one who had fought on the Sublicius Bridge by the side of Horatius Cocles the day they saved Rome from King Porsenna. And there was Marcus Valerius, brother of Publius, who swore that by Lake Regillus he would finish the glorious work that Publicola had begun for Rome, for Publius Valerius had, with Brutus, driven away Tarquin and all his house.

The battle began. At the first onset King Tarquin leveled his lance and rode against Aulus. From the Roman front line Titus Aebutius spurred his horse against Octavius Mamilius.

But before King Tarquin could reach Aulus, he received a wound in his left side. His officers anxiously gathered around him, but they had to carry the old King from the field of battle. Titus and Octavius crashed against each other lance to lance. Titus struck Mamilius on the breast, and Mamilius ran his lance through Titus' right arm.

Titus was compelled to withdraw from the battle, for his
arm could no longer hold the spear nor the sword; Mamilius,
however, ignored his wound.

Soon the Latins were giving ground. Mamilius called out
to the banished Romans of the Tarquinian household and
sent them into the thick of the fight. They made such a fierce
onrush that no man or horse could stand before them, so
bitterly had those exiles drunk of the cup of revenge against
the opponents who had deprived them of their properties and
rights.

The battle was going slowly. The two phalanxes had advanced, almost to within fighting range, but still they held
their charge. It was as though the two armies themselves were
witnessing the single combats of their leaders in a duel that
was to decide the redemption of King Tarquin or the final
triumph of the republic.

Marcus Valerius leveled his lance and galloped against
Tarquin's son, Titus. Titus drew back, sheltering amidst his
officers, and Marcus rode after him in fury and plunged into
the midst of the enemy. A Latin officer ran his lance into his
side as he was rushing on, but Marcus' horse galloped on
until Marcus dropped dead to the ground.

At this, the Tarquinians side-charged more vehemently,
and the front ranks of the Romans vacillated and turned in
fright. Aulus, their leader, rode up with his picked squadron
and ordered his men to level their lances and slay all whose
faces were toward them, whether friends or foe.

The Romans stopped their flight, and Aulus Postumius
prayed aloud and vowed that he would raise a temple to
Castor and Pollux, the twin sons of Zeus, if the Dioscuri
would aid him to win the battle. And to his troops he promised that the first two men to break the enemy lines would
receive the richest of rewards.

No sooner had Aulus spoken his prayer than two unknown
horsemen appeared at the head of his squadron. Their horses
were white as snow and the riders were taller and fairer than

any man. They were in the first bloom of youth, and no one had seen them before.

The two fair horsemen took the lead, and a fierce battle ensued. Octavius Mamilius came up to the rescue of the Tarquinii, but Titus Herminius ran his spear through his body and killed him at one blow. As he was despoiling him of his beautiful armor, he himself was struck by a javelin and was borne off the field, and died.

Still the two mysterious horsemen on their snow-white steeds kept riding before the Roman army. The enemy was fleeing before them, the Tarquinians were beaten down and slain, and Titus Tarquinius was among the killed. The Romans pursued the Latins into their camp, and the two men on the white horses were still at their head.

After the camp was taken and the battle fully won, Aulus Postumius sought out the two horsemen to give them the promised reward. But they could not be found either among the victorious troops nor among the dead. Only upon a hard black rock there were seen the marks of a horse's hoofs—marks of a kind no earthly horse had ever made. Those marks remained imprinted upon the rock in after ages.

Thus the great battle of Lake Regillus ended as the sun went down.

In Rome, the people knew only that the two huge armies had joined battle; and as the day wore on, all longed for tidings. Suddenly, in the twilight, people lingering in the forum saw two horsemen, taller and fairer than the tallest and fairest of men, on horses white as snow. They looked as if they had just come from the battle, and their snowy horses were covered with sweat. The two horsemen alighted by the temple of Vesta, where a spring of water bubbled and filled a small pool, and there they washed away the stains of battle.

When the onlookers crowded around them and asked for news, the two horsemen told how the battle had been fought and how it was won. Having thus spoken, they again mounted their horses and rode away, and were seen no more.

Thus the Roman people understood that Castor and Pollux, the twin sons of Zeus, had answered Aulus Postumius' prayer, had fought for Rome and defeated her enemies, and with more than mortal speed had borne the news of the victory to Rome.

Therefore, Aulus built a beautiful temple to Castor and Pollux. The rich rewards, promised to the two who first broke the enemy lines, he gave as offerings to the new shrine, for truly the Dioscuri had won the battle for Rome.

VI

King Tarquin attended the funeral of his son and his son-in-law Octavius Mamilius; and then he went to Cuma and begged his friend Aristodemus, the tyrant of Cuma, to allow him to end his life there in meditation.

He lived a few more years, contemplating the events that had caused his downfall—and he thought that his fate was a sign of the destiny that was expressed in the Prophecy of the Etruscan Century of glory and power, after which Rome would have her span of twelve Etruscan years. He believed that the rape of Lucrece was not the real cause of the downfall of the Tarquinian house: the ravishing of a woman was not a sufficiently important reason. The real cause was Brutus—the viper that he, King Tarquin, had foolishly nursed in his bosom. His grandfather the Priscus had ended a family feud by declassing Brutus the Elder, and he, Tarquin the Proud, should not have shown pity on the son and brought up Lucius Brutus with his own family, for gratitude is a plant that does not grow in a king's garden!

As for democracy and the people's republic—well, the Romans would soon find out to their cost the penalties of a people's government. For freedom is not a purchasable commodity but a virtue that exists only in the soul of some rare men who have intellect enough to create a free world of their own; but it cannot be applied to masses and peoples.

A traveler brought news to King Tarquin that on the day the Romans had dedicated the temple of Castor and Pollux, celebrating the great victory of Lake Regillus, an Etruscan augur announced that republican Rome would run a span of twelve Etruscan years until another king would come, who, however, should not wear a crown: one hundred days before he would be proclaimed king, lightning would strike from his statue in the forum the first letter of his name, Caesar, and "C" days after this omen he would ascend, assassinated by another Brutus, amongst the gods—"Aesar." [1]

At last King Tarquin peacefully died, ninety years old, leaving to Aristodemus his worldly wealth, for all his sons had died—the progeny of the Tarquins was now extinct. And the Etruscans, on learning of his death, deemed that the last descendant of Tarchun the Founder deserved to be buried in the mausoleum of his forefathers. Therefore, from the twelve lucumonies the representatives of the lars came to Cuma, and begged Aristodemus' permission to take away with them the body of King Tarquin for honorable burial.

They dressed the body in his full armor, with the breast-plate of gold that was so beautifully chased; and they put upon his head the kingly crown; and they carried the spoils of King Tarquin to Tarquinia, taking care to by-pass the hateful Rome.

In the capital city of Etruria, the augurs and the priests and all the lars escorted the bier of Tarquin along the Via Inferi. The funeral procession halted at the tomb of the Founder, and only the princes of the Twelve Cities joined in the cortege that descended into the vault.

For the occasion, the house of the dead was brightly lit by torches, as was proper for the reception of the last of the Tarquins. All around the rooms, the images resting on their

---

1 In the Etruscan language, Aesar meant gods.

left elbows upon their tombs, some with their wives by their sides, all beautifully arrayed and with serene expression, looked on like guests on their couches at a great banquet.

On the appointed bed of stone, in the place of honor at the end of the central room, the bier of Tarquin the Proud was laid to rest. With his own hands the chief augur directed the priests who hung above the bed the enormous shield of the King and his greaves and his mighty sword. Then they placed upon the bier a stupendous statue of the last of the Etruscans, cast in pure gold.

EPILOGUE

I

From the day that the Dioscuri gave Rome the victory over the spirit of Tarquinia, a terrible revenge befell the Etruscans.

Tinia the Benevolent had truly transferred his favors to his new temple of Jupiter Capitolinus.

Rome was a republic. She could now run her own course, to follow her belief in the divine predestination to create a higher order of things in the Mediterranean world. But her vengeance against the Etruscans was perpetuated relentlessly. Centuries later, the historians called it the triumph of democracy; but it emanated from the vengeance of one embittered man, Lucius Brutus.

The battles of freedom have only too often been fought to satisfy the wrath of vengeance of some demagogue, and no despotism is so fearful as that which speaks in the name of the people's liberty.

In Rome, not long after the foundation of the republic, it happened that the populus—that was, actually, the ancient patrician body—and the plebs, who were now supposed to have seized power within the body politic, stood more than ever arrayed against each other like two unrelated races; and between them there could not possibly be any unity of feeling or equality of rights.

Conditions under the new republic were similar to those which prevailed in Greece under what was called the Eupatridian rule. While the people were drunk with victory, the senate and the patricians had taken upon themselves the spoils of royalty. They flattered the people, told the people that nothing would be done without their assent: "The real government of Rome is in the hands of the good people, the great family of the people."

The people were pampered. But Tarquin's death exposed the real secret of the revolution. The fiery and proud patricians reappeared, and a Tarquin resurrected in each of them birth, wealth, and all those dignities of which the patricians were exclusive possessors and which marked the democratic line between the Augustan order and the vile plebeians. The people received nothing but travail, poverty and subjection; lucky to find work, lucky to vegetate and to precipitate themselves in servile manner into the mud, bending their backs before an insulting patronage. The people had fought to conquer new lands for the republic; but the patricians alone got the reward.

The people had returned from the Tarquinian war bearing wounds and scars; miserable, reduced to penury, whilst new patrician laws gave additional rights to the usurers and lenders, and the debtors were turned into slaves, and beaten with the cat-o'-nine-tails. The "Sovereign People," in whose name servitude was imposed upon the vanquished, moaned in Rome under the iron republican rule. The people had chased away the tyrant without chasing away tyranny.

The supreme power which had been formerly vested in the king, had now passed into the hands of a magistracy whose members were appointed by vote. These republican officials, commonly called consuls, were given the title of praetors. The weight of the civil, military and judicial authority that had passed from the king to the heads of the republic, became considerably lessened by the action of causes that were, from their very nature, bound to make themselves more and more strongly felt.

Two consuls were placed at the head of the state in order that the actions of one might be under the restraining influence of the other's veto. And the term of this highest office was never longer than one year.[1] This system of one-year tenure of office was soon found to have grave defects; but so much a part was it of the patrician as well as the democratic republicanism that it never occurred to anyone to change it. The greatest disadvantage was that the yearly tenure of office gave rise to a class of permanent officials, the civil service of the scribes, who came to be of paramount importance in the conduct of public affairs.

Equally in time of war, when naturally every head of the republic did not show equal qualifications for military leadership, the command of the army was given to some experienced general who was specially appointed for the campaign.

Moreover, when a consul was confronted by great and unexpected difficulties, he was empowered by the senate to appoint the best man of the state as dictator. This dictator was in his turn entitled to select as his assistant a Master of the Horse—Magister Equitum. The dictatorship was, in the beginning, for a term of only six months, and controlled all minor offices. But it soon happened that as the dictator could not be held accountable, and as there was no appeal against his decision, the patricians frequently had recourse, during the course of internal struggles, to the appointment of a dictator in order to quell the plebeian opposition. And while the consuls were preceded by twelve lictors, the dictator was given twenty-four, like the king in former days.

Owing to the constant increase in the volume of public affairs, the consuls appointed deputies for the performance of certain duties, whose term expired with their own; and associated with the consuls were two quaestors, who were in charge of the state archives and treasury, and with the prose-

---

[1] It was from this system that the calling of the years from the consuls' names came into usage.

cution of criminals; while two commissioners were appointed to judge cases of sedition and high treason.

The consuls' power however suffered from two limitations, which arose from the altered position of the senate toward them. According to formal law, the senators stood in the same relations to the consuls as they did to the king, being not over but under the heads of the republic, who every four years, on the occasion of the assessment of taxes, revised the list of senators and appointed new ones to fill whatever vacancies had occurred.

Gradually, but ever more forcefully, began to be felt the enormous predominance held by large aristocratic corporations, whose members, all men of great political experience, had a life-long tenure of office as against officials who were appointed only for a single year. The senate represented the unity and the firmly established tradition of Roman politics and rule. Not even the proud self-consciousness of the consuls could prevent their office from coming to be considered as merely the executive organ of the senate.

The people's assemblies, too, had since the creation of the republic assumed a new character and a different position. The necessity of the governing power, after the overthrow of the Tarquins, to make sure of the sympathy of the lower classes, had brought into much greater prominence the centuriate assembly—in which both patricians and plebeians were bound together in making important decisions. The functions of this body extended now to the election of consuls, to the ratification or rejection of measures proposed by the higher government, to the declaration of war, and lastly to the exercise of jurisdiction in criminal cases where appeal was permitted from the sentence of the quaestors.

But the plebeians found that, under the new order, all the advantages fell to the patricians.

The patricians might have avoided the one hundred and fifty years' struggle between the two classes, had they risen above their prejudices and taken into their own circles the more nearly related plebeian families, admitting them to

equal marriage rights, to seats in the senate, and to eligibility
for the various public offices; and if they had further opened
the state's domains to the mass of plebeians. Instead, the patricians displayed the most obdurate selfishness and greed—
traits manifested in no lesser degree by their plebeian kindred.

Thus it came about that not long after the foundation of
the republic, the patrician body—the populus—and the plebeians stood against each other like two unrelated races. The
election of consuls was by no means carried out by free vote.
A list of nominees was made out beforehand by the presiding
consul and the senate, from which the voters must choose,
having at most the right to reject candidates without that of
substituting other names. The curiate assembly of the patricians alone had the right to confer, by the passage of a Lex
Curiata de imperio, the supreme power upon the successful
candidate.

There was further the extreme severity shown in leaving
tax-free the money capital of the patricians, while in the case
of the plebeians no allowance was made for mortgages on
their property. Furthermore, the wars conducted since the
expulsion of the Tarquins had pressed hard upon the plebeians. The successive calls to arms, the devastation of their
lands, together with the heavy war tax, formed an insupport-
able burden which was but little relieved by the declaration
that the increase in impost would be regarded as a mere
temporary advance, to be returned at a later period. The
poorer leaseholders were heavily in debt; the legal rate of
interest was enormously high—so high that it was welcomed
by the plebeians as a great relief when later (a century and a
half later, 357 B.C.) it was reduced to 10 per cent. In case of
failure to pay, the accumulated interest was added to the
original debt until the amount owed was increased to an
overwhelming figure. Hence, the first attack of the common
people on the patrician class was made on the ground of the
extreme harshness of the laws governing debt. The creditor
had complete possession of the person of the debtor, who fre-

quently preferred taking advantage of the nexum and placed himself in bondage to the creditor to serve him as many years as were required to liquidate the debt, or until the creditor actually sold him as a slave in a foreign land.

In the year 495 B.C. the dissatisfaction reached a momentous pitch. The plebs, unable to bear further maltreatment, consented to serve only under the Dictator Marcus Valerius, who was beloved by the people. But when his proposals for a modification of the laws against debtors fell through in the senate, the patience of the plebeians ended, and the plebeian portion of the army withdrew to the Sacred Mount, on the peninsula formed outside Rome by the junction of the Anio and Tiber rivers.

The seriousness of the situation finally obliged the patricians and the senate to yield, and a compact was reached, the effects of which were felt even as late as the imperial epoch. The two branches of the population, to which was given an international form, stipulated that the plebeians residing in the state should be organized into an independent body, having their own official representatives that were to equal in power those of the patricians. In opposition to the consuls were placed two plebeian tribunes, later increased to four. Guardians of the community, their aediles being at the service of the plebeians as police and general administration agents, the tribunes of the plebs had the right and duty to protect their fellow plebeians against injustice and maladministration, and to uphold the right of appeal—in a word, to interfere whenever the rights of the plebs seemed in danger. The people had thus won—with this paradoxical result, however, that, as time would show, the more ambitious among the aristocratic young men would win power by courting the people, and, by buying the favor and the votes of the people, be elected tribunes of the plebs. The corruption of democracy was well on the way.

The taxation abuses and the tyranny of the laws regulating debt, as well as the monopoly by patricians of state domains, brought about the agrarian reforms proposed by Spurius Cassius. The public lands were to be surveyed and given out in grants to the poorer plebeians, and the remaining portions rented to patricians under much stricter conditions of payment than formerly. The Lex Cassia was passed, but it remained a dead letter for thirty years. Out of revenge, the accusation was hurled against Cassius, an accusation fatal in republican Rome, of having aspired to mount the throne; and in the year following the expiration of his term of office he was sentenced to death.

The civil strife went on till, in the year 457 B.C., the number of the tribunes of the plebs was increased to ten, called decemvirs, and eventually, in 451, a new code of laws, both civil and criminal, was approved by the senate and accepted by the Comitia Centuriata, and affixed on ten copper tables to the speakers' rostrum in the forum. Those tables became eventually the Twelve Tables which, for centuries, were considered the foundation of all law, always mentioned by Cicero with the utmost reverence. In those Twelve Tables the Roman people now had a just and equal code of civil and criminal laws.

But they were the only legacy of the decemvirs, who, headed by Appius Claudius, soon became intolerable despots. The name of Appius Claudius remained forever infamous in Roman history for the episode of Virginia, who was stabbed to death by her plebeian father rather than let her fall to Appius Claudius' lust. The episode did not lead to a war, but it was marked by another withdrawal of the Plebeians *en masse* to the Sacred Mount on the River Anio, a secession that forced the decemvirs to resign.

The greatest and finest pages of republican Rome were written in those years. Names that became legend—Coriolanus, Cincinnatus, the Fabii: names and deeds that fired the imagination of poets and dramatists throughout the ages. Those were the years that marked the assertion of Rome as the dominant power; the years of the Roman conquest of Italy, and the decline and fall of Etruria.

The first, the fiercest, was the war against Veii. It lasted eighty years, and the final siege of Veii was regarded by the Romans as an epic great as the legendary siege of Troy. Like the Hellenic poets who had sung of the Trojan War, three centuries afterward the imagination of the proud Roman annalists embroidered upon the never-ending battle against the Etruscan city, a campaign that was of foremost importance in the life of young Rome, with episodes that mingled fact and myth.

The war commenced around the year 271 of Rome. The close of the fifth century B.C. marked the beginning of the great conflicts between Rome and the great Etruscan city just outside her borders. The territories of Veii had often been a place of refuge for the Roman malcontents and turbulent nobles, such as the sons of Cincinnatus and others, and it is very possible that the Roman consuls and leaders, who began this lengthy contest, may have had many private piques to avenge. The Romans were the first aggressors, in order to employ and keep in check their own plebeians; and oftener the war brought disaster to them rather than glory. And yet, the list of Rome's great generals opens with the name of the conqueror of Veii.

At first, the two consuls, Caeso Fabius and Spurius Furius, were defeated. Their army fled, threw away their arms and retreated within the city, the Veientines following them to the very gates and taking an immense number of prisoners, horses and arms. And the next year the war was so unpopular in Rome that the plebs refused to enlist.

Again the Romans were defeated with Manlius Fabius and Cincinnatus commanding an army of twenty thousand men. Fabius' tent was struck by lightning—a clear sign of Jupiter's disfavor, which induced him to quit his camp, whereupon the Etruscans immediately seized it with all the booty of the Romans. The next year, Rome was in such imminent danger that the reserve troops and the city militia were called out and all the men that could be spared were sent by the colonies, the subject towns and the allies.

In the fourth year the Fabii, being no longer the ruling house among the patricians, with the rank and power of consul secured to them, resolved to be the ruling house in opposition, and became the patrons and protectors of the plebs. But the Roman army kept so resolutely to their trenches that the Veientine cavalry came and defied them every day. At last the insults of the enemy took effect, and as both consuls showed distrust of their troops, for a defeat at the gates of Rome would have been the ruin of the city, the men threatened to elect other commanders who would not be afraid of them. The consuls then pretended to yield, only requiring every man to swear that he would conquer or die, and the Roman army was led forth to battle. "They fought," says Livy, "hand to hand and sword to sword," yet Quintus Fabius, the general's brother, was killed by an Etruscan who, of course, was represented as a giant. At the death of this great hero the Romans were panic-stricken and gave way on every side, until Marcus Fabius leapt over his brother's body, and with the help of Caeso Fabius routed that part of the Etruscan army.

The battle ended undecided—but Marcus Fabius succeeded in securing his brother's body and that of his colleague Manlius. Drawing off his troops in order, he claimed a victory which, however, is belied by what followed. The Roman senate offered him a triumph, but he sensibly declined it— doubtless because the Etruscan giant who had killed his brother was still alive. And he preferred to enter Rome in mourning.[1] Subsequently the Fabian clan left Rome and retired, with some five thousand followers, to a spot near the River Cremera, a neutral zone between Rome and Veii, where they settled and built a fort. But the Porta Carmentalis by which they had left the city was forever afterward called the Porta Scelerata. In due course the fort of the Gabii

---

[1] Dionysius.

was destroyed, and five thousand were killed or taken slaves into Veii, and the fate of the Fabii was so lamented that no Roman would ever pass through the Porta Scelerata.

When the war recommenced, Veii had made an alliance with the Sabines. At the end of nine years a peace was concluded, and the Veientines agreed to supply Rome with corn, which Veii had in abundance.

Many years elapsed after the termination of the Fabian war with Veii, during which we know nothing of any of the states of Etruria further than that they kept up their prodigious walls, fortifications and roads; continued their annual fairs and religious processions; and attended to their internal navigation and the working order of their wonderful drains and subterranean canals.

They still commanded the Tyrrhenian and Adriatic seas and carried on a flourishing commerce; and we can presume they were at peace with each other, because their political union remained unbroken until after the fall of Veii. About the year 438 B.C. Rome was afflicted with one of her frequent famines which caused rioting throughout the city. The situation was saved by Etruria, whose agriculture, thanks to the perfect irrigation. was always rich in crops and harvests.

It happened that the very next year, Fidene revolted against Rome and placed herself once more under the protection of her mother city Veii. The Lar Tolumnius was at this time King of Veii, and the Romans sent four feciales to him, to complain of his favoring their rebels and to demand satisfaction. Tolumnius, most inexcusably, advised some of the Fidenians to seize the feciales and put them to death. A bloody war followed. Tolumnius himself led his troops into the field, and fought a hard battle with the Consul Lucius Sergius. In haste the senate created Mamercus Emilius dictator, with Lucius Cincinnatus, son of the celebrated commander, as his master of the cavalry. Fidene was retaken and, to the amazement and joy of the Romans, the great parliament of Voltumna decided to refuse aid to the King of Veii, alleging that Tolumnius had begun the war on his own private account, without first asking their consent. After the death of Tolumnius the Romans were glad to accept a peace with Veii for twenty years.

Those twenty years of peace were years of continued fear for the Romans; fear that their contests with the nations on the other side of the Tiber might tempt the Etruscans to break the treaty. But political dissensions and discontentment had spread in Veii after the death of Lar Tolumnius. The senate of Veii had tried a new form of government with consuls, as Rome had done; and the year in which the war should have recommenced Veii was in such a state of unrest that her rulers would very gladly have deferred it, and they sent ambassadors to Rome to express their willingness, on certain terms, to prolong the peace.

Seven saecula of Etruscan time had now run their course, each saeculum averaging one hundred and ten years. The eighth had commenced, and very early in this period the first history of Etruria was written, being compiled from the dry but carefully preserved pontifical annals of the various states of the Etruscan League and from the names and dates which marked the principal temples. Perhaps the Etruscans were moved to attempt this kind of composition by the example of Herodotus; and it is a most curious fact that their literature received its first great impulse when their political power was visibly on the decline. It was almost an omen.

It happened that the Romans sent four feciales to Veii to declare that they did not consider the terms quite equal, and that the Veientine senate must propose better conditions if friendship was to be maintained. To Rome's amazement the senate of Veii replied that unless the feciales were contented with the terms already offered and left the city instantly, they would treat them as Lar Tolumnius had treated their predecessors.

War was declared. A full meeting was convened by the Etruscans at the fanum of Voltumna, to decide whether the rest of Etruria was required to give assistance to Veii. In the great national diet the Veientines themselves were divided into two parties, and the diet adjourned leaving the question undecided. It was a fatal mistake, for the result of the war of Rome against Veii marked the end of Etruria.

The war lasted for years. The Veientines, remembering their former victories under their kings, returned to the monarchial form, which was the Etruscan tradition. But the prince they selected was as unpopular as he was arrogant and impious. The national diet of Voltumna again assembled and passed a decree that no assistance should be given to Veii as long as the city continued under the government of this unworthy lucumon. It is strange that the name of this prince should have passed into oblivion, unregistered by Etruscan or Roman annalists alike.

Once again the Roman plebs were far from eager to fight a new war in the field. The infantry complained, through their tribunes, that their tents and huts were covered with frost and snow, and that while they were forced in these conditions to be forever on the alert they had the vexation of seeing the Etruscans, when the daily skirmish was over, retire to their strong city on the heights where they warmed themselves by their cheerful fires, within solid stone walls, close to their wives and children. The plebeian leaders actually made an attempt to have the army withdrawn, and only the celebrated eloquence of Appius Claudius succeeded in keeping the army together by the sound argument: "If you withdraw, Veii will so arrange her affairs that she will bring against us the power of all Etruria." Claudius further pressed upon the plebeian leaders that their army had, at a vast expense, enclosed Veii with immense works, actually confining the enemy within their walls, so that they could not till their lands. If the Roman troops were now withdrawn, the Veientines would demolish these works and make reprisals on the Roman territories.

The Roman troops remained in camp, hard at work increasing their fortifications, and the siege of Veii continued, apparently endlessly, until a new winter came, so severe that the Tiber was frozen over and the shivering troops clamored again that their enemies' lot was a better one.

It was the eighth year of the war. Rome was suffering from a famine and pestilence. Many prodigious events occurred; the Lake of Alba, which was at that time 200 feet higher than it is at present, swelled and rose without any visible cause of melting snows or violent rains, and the waters continued to rise and rise, though the weather was fair and dry. The Sibylline Books were consulted, a lectisternium was ordered as an expiation to three Etruscan and three Greek gods—Erkle, Turms and Minerva, Apollo, Latona and Diana; but without avail.

The Romans could get no haruspex to tell them the meaning of the strange event, for the Magi of the Etruscans had withdrawn from Rome during this implacable war, and none of the Roman augurs had science enough to explain it.

Then somebody recalled that an aged Veientine haruspex, who had run away from the besieged city, had foretold that Veii could not be taken till the water of the Alban Lake should be brought into a channel. This haruspex, whom some called Aquilex, meaning director of the water works, was sought out; and he advised the Romans to reduce the level of the lake by the usual method of an emissarium (a subterranean channel for drainage). This was laboriously done; and the emissarium was built with such consummate skill that it still functions, and it has never required more than partial repair in the course of twenty-four centuries. It consists of a tunnel cut through the hill of the present town of Castel Gandolfo, and when the water again reaches the open air, it is dispersed in many channels through the fields for irrigation. Only two men can work abreast in the channel together; but seven air holes are pierced from the ground above down to it; and if workmen were let down by these, several pairs could carry on their operations at the same time.

The war was finally decided by this feat of engineering and by the valor of the Dictator Furius Camillus, who, guided by the same Veientine Aquilex, mined a tunnel which burrowed beneath the walls of Veii. From the moment the tunneling was started, Camillus always spoke of Veii as if it were already in his possession. He inflamed his troops with his enthusiasm. He even sent to ask the senate in Rome what he should do with the spoils, until at last he vowed one-tenth of all the spoils to Apollo, the famous and most beautiful Apollo of Veii, and implored Juno-Kupra, the patron goddess of Veii, to transfer her residence to Rome and to come and reign there.

"Led by thee, O Pythian Apollo, and inspired by thy spirit, I go to destroy the city of Veii; therefore unto thee I vow the tenth part of the prey; and to thee, in like manner, O Juno Regina, who now protectest Veii, do I pray that thou permit us to bear thee to our city and make it for the future thine. There a temple shall receive thee, worthy of thy greatness."

This ceremony over, and the tunnel being finished and ready to spring, Camillus gave the command for the final assault. The Veientines had been so lulled into security by the apparent inactivity and stubborn presumption of Camillus, that they had laughed at him. When their gates were seized and opened by the Roman army, their king was in the citadel preparing a sacrifice to Juno.

Camillus marched into the temple and killed the king with his own hand. The fight then became so desperate that the women and their slaves mounted up to the roofs of the houses and poured down boiling oil and firebrands upon the Roman soldiers in the streets.

At last Veii surrendered, yielding herself not to the might of her enemy but to fate. She was the most opulent city of the Etruscan name, and showed the majesty of her greatness even in the hour of her destruction. One hundred thousand souls were contained within her walls. She was as large and fine as Athens, and far richer and more beautiful than Rome. When her spoils came to be estimated, they far surpassed the utmost estimate that Camillus had formed of them.

The day after the capitulation of the city Camillus sold the free inhabitants by auction as slaves. When all human wealth

had been carried away from Veii, the dictator ordered that all
the temple's offerings be removed. Camillus was so amazed
at his conquest that he thought the heavens themselves would
envy him his fortune, and lifting his hand upward he prayed
that if either gods or men required some counterpoise to a
success so brilliant, would they visit it on him alone and not
on the Roman people. Having said this he turned around
and fell, which was taken as an omen that evil by the sword
would ere long visit him and also his city, which was sup-
posedly fulfilled in the taking of Rome by the Gauls a very
few years after.

The gods Apollo and Juno were removed to Rome: Camillus bowed low before Juno-Kupra, supplicated her forgiveness and requested her to remove with all honor to Rome
and there reign as a queen. The image moved her head in
assent; it was said that she also smiled, and upon this Camillus appointed some of his handsomest young men to wash
their bodies and array themselves in white garments, and to
bear the image of Juno with careful reverence to a shrine
already prepared upon the Aventine.

Veii was now deserted by her gods, and Rome made certain
that she could never rise again. Certain it was that the cry,
"Delenda est Etruria!" was in the Roman hearts before the
same dreadful sentence was breathed from the lips of him
who was to pronounce from the darkest depths of his inmost
soul—*"Delenda est Cartago!"*

The destruction of Etruria was now on. As Veii had submitted on terms, Camillus was bound not to destroy the
buildings, public or private. Her houses and palaces were
finer than those of Rome; but Camillus was resolved that
they should never again be inhabited or kept up. He reduced
the wealthy to poverty, the free to slavery, and he decreed
that ruin should be the doom of Veii and that time should
crumble her to dust: that she should be abandoned to destruction and neglect, that the owl should roost in the chamber of her kings. The decree of destruction went so far that
when the plebeians of Rome, and even some of the patricians,

wished to better their condition by removing to Veii, Camillus opposed it, as if the object of the whole war would thus be rendered useless: *"Etruria delenda est!"*

The Romans were now masters of a city larger and richer than their own, and their territories and population were nearly doubled. Camillus endeavored to collect the tenth of the spoils which he had vowed to Apollo, but as he had been obliged to allow his soldiers to plunder at will on the surrender of Veii, he had no means of estimating the booty, and he laid it upon each man's conscience to tax himself. As the troops were highly indignant, Camillus declared that his vow included both the buildings of Veii and the newly conquered land, and insisted that the tenth's value of the whole property must be represented by a golden offering of eight talents of weight, to be sent to the temple of Apollo in Delphi. As the gold was not forthcoming, the Roman matrons brought in their bracelets and earrings to the amount required. The metal was weighed, valued and paid for, and then manufactured into a great golden bowl; and the senate, in acknowledgment of this meritorious conduct in their ladies, decreed that the matrons should henceforth be permitted to drive in open carriages through the streets every day, and in covered ones at all the games and on every festival.

II

At the time of the passage of the Roman eagles upon the right bank of the Tiber the destruction of Etruria was settled. Rome was now bent on blotting out from Italy the Etruscan civilization from which she herself had sprung. Still Etruria was unconscious of the dark tempest looming on her horizon; still she was confident in the splendor of a power and greatness that were soon to crumble to dust. One year after the fall of Veii the Romans opened the road to the north. Rome was now a threatening wedge between the Etruscan littoral and the inland—Rome was now on the frontier of Tarquinia. And a much darker storm was brewing from the north, against both Etruria and Rome. The darkest battles for survival were to be fought, events that were a return to the primeval ages.

One would say that for two hundred years after the fall of Tarquin the Proud the entire course of history worked against Etruria.

We come now to a period in which Roman courage and fortitude were put to the severest test. The course of Roman history, hitherto disturbed only by petty border wars, now suffered from a great convulsion—the invasion of Italy by the Gauls.

The Gauls were a tribe of that large race known as the Celts, who at that time peopled nearly the whole of western Europe, from the heart of Germany to the ocean. The northern and central parts of the continent were in the hands of a people known by the common name of Germans or Teutons, to whom belonged the Goths, Saxons, Danes, Normans, Lombards, Franks and Alamanni, while the Celts possessed the western parts of the continent, from the Iberian Peninsula up to France and the British Isles. There were two main divisions of Celts—Gael and Cymri; the Gauls inhabited France and Spain. Large bodies of Gauls had already passed over the Alps into Italy, overrunning the rich northern plains, occupying the territory which lies between the Alps, the Apennines and the Adriatic, which the Romans later called Gallia Cisalpina. The northern Etruscans gave way before these fierce barbarians, and then the Gauls crossed the Apennines into southern Etruria, and came into first contact with Rome. The commonly accepted date for this event is 390 B.C. How long before this the Gallic hordes had been pouring into Italy we do not know.

The tribe that crossed the Apennines were Senones, or Celts—large-limbed, with fair skin, yellow hair and blue eyes, in all respects quite different from the natives of southern Italy. Their courage was high, but they were more fitted for action than endurance, able to conquer but not steady enough to maintain their conquests.

It was said and sung that Brennus, the Gauls' chief, and his barbarians passed into Etruria at the invitation of Aruns of Clusium, whose wife had been seduced by the young lucumo of that city. To avenge his private wrongs the Etruscan Aruns called in the Gauls, as Count Julian in the Spanish romance called in the Moors to avenge the seduction of his daughter by Roderic the Goth.

Aruns not being able to raise a civil war with any prospect of success, and burning with indignation, turned to the Gauls and invited them to settle in his own fruitful country. He did not solicit any of those tribes which had long kept the fron-

tiers in alarm from Perugia up to Luna. He went directly to
Gallia Cisalpina, the cradle of the race—to Mediolanum,
which they had built in the vast plain under the northern
Alps.

Invited by Aruns, Brennus and his Gauls crossed the Apennines and laid siege to Clusium. The Etruscans, terrified and
helpless, despairing of effectual succor from their own countrymen of the federation, sent to seek aid from the hated city
on the Tiber that had by now conquered so many old Etruscan cities. In face of the common danger, Rome determined
to support the Etruscans against the Gauls. However, all the
senate did was to send three ambassadors to warn the Gauls
not to meddle further with Clusium, for Clusium was an ally
of Rome.

The Gauls took no notice, and continued the war. It happened that a battle was fought while the Roman ambassadors
were still at Clusium, and they, forgetting their peaceful role
of envoys, took part with the Clusians against the Gauls. The
Gauls, in high wrath, demanded to be led straight against
the city whose ambassadors were so faithless. Brennus restrained them, and sent an embassy to Rome demanding that
the envoys should be given up. The senate referred such a
weighty matter to the people, and at the comitia the people,
in derision of the "barbarians," elected the three envoys at
Clusium to be military tribunes.

On hearing of this gross and open insult, Brennus broke
camp at Clusium and led his Gauls against Rome. The Gallic
hordes burst upon Latium like a thunderstorm. At a battle
on the small River Allia, in the Sabine Hills, the Romans
were defeated and, seized with panic, they fled, many being
drowned in the Tiber. Only a remnant of the army returned
to Rome. Brennus was at the gates of Rome.

So sudden a victory held even the Gauls in a state of stupe-
faction. At first they feared a strategem; but they began to
collect the spoils and to pile up the arms of the slain, as was
their custom. Then, at length, when no sign of anything hos-

tile was anywhere observed, they reached the city of Rome not long before sunset. Some horsemen brought back word that the gates were not shut and that no guards were posted, and there were no armed troops on the walls. This was another cause of amazement and, dreading the night, the Gauls camped between the city and the River Anio.

When the yells and clangor of the Gauls' arms outside the gates were heard, the Romans imagined the Gauls would attack them before nightfall; then, it was reckoned that the assault was deferred until night, in order to strike the greatest terror.

During the night, with no hope of defending the city, for only a small number of troops now remained, it was decided that all youths fit for service and the able-bodied senators with their wives and children should retire into the citadel and Capitol, and there they should defend the gods and the city and the name of Rome. The flamens and the vestals would carry away the objects of religion, and continue their worship until no one remained. The flamens and the vestal virgins, however, unable to carry away all the sacred objects, considered it best to put them into casks and they buried them in the chapel adjoining the residence of the flamens, where it was considered profane to spit. The rest they carried away along the road which led by the Sublician Bridge, to the Janiculum.

In the city, the aged persons returned to their houses and awaited the enemy with their minds prepared for death. Such of them who had occupied curule offices, in order that they might die with the insignia of their station, arrayed themselves in their most splendid garments and seated themselves in their ivory chairs in the middle of their halls.

The calamity came with daylight—but it did not take the form they expected. For the Gauls, either because the night had abated the angry feelings or because they were now confronted with a city that had not to be taken by storm, entered Rome quietly, through the Colline Gate which lay open, advanced into the forum, casting their eyes around on the temples and on the citadel which alone exhibited any appearance of defense. Then, after leaving a small guard, they disappeared in search of plunder. They found the streets entirely deserted, and the houses open to them.

This solitude appalled them. They returned in groups into the forum, and there, in the halls of the leading citizens, they beheld the men sitting in the porches of the palaces—men who, with their ornaments and garments and the majesty of their appearance, looked almost like gods. While they were thus gazing at them, one Gaul stroked the long beard of Marcus Papirius. The venerable Papirius answered by hitting the Gaul on the head with his ivory stick. This started the slaughter. The eminent citizens were promptly slain in their seats. After the slaughter of the nobles no person was spared; the houses were plundered and set on fire. The first sacking of Rome by the "barbarians" was thus accomplished.

The Gauls, when they saw that among the fires and ruins of the captured city nothing remained except armed enemies, determined to make an attack on the citadel. At break of day their entire forces were marshaled in the forum; and after raising the war cry and forming a testudo (overlapping their shields above their heads), they advanced. About the middle of the ascent the Romans met them, making a charge from their higher ground. They routed the Gauls with such slaughter that never again did the Gauls try that kind of attack.

Some of the Gauls then marched from the city to try the Romans at Ardea, where Camillus was in exile. The former dictator, filled with grief at the plight of Rome, and wondering what had become of those men who with him had taken Veii, went forth to meet the Gauls. It was an unprotected camp. Camillus caught the Gauls in sleep and it was not a battle but slaughter.

Meanwhile at Rome the siege was slow, and there was quiet on both sides, the Gauls being intent only on preventing the Romans from escaping. Suddenly a Roman youth, Caius Fabius Dorso, descended from the Capitol, carrying in his hands the sacred utensils, passed out through the midst of the enemy's post, and reached the Quirinal Hill. After performing the solemn rites, he came back by the same way with the same firm countenance, confident that the gods were propitious, and returned to the Capitol to rejoin his friends. There was a belief that it was the duty of the Fabian family to solemnize a sacrifice on the Quirinal Hill in needful times. The Romans were fired with enthusiasm at the exploit: it put them in mind of the great deed of Camillus and the men who had fought under him. Camillus was sent for from Ardea.

But the citadel and the Capitol were in great danger. The Gauls, following the track of the messenger sent by Camillus to confirm his coming help, tried the way up to the Capitol. The sacred geese of Juno gave the alarm. Marcus Manlius was awakened by their cackling and clapping of their wings, and snatching up his arms he struck with the boss of his shield a Gaul who had already got a footing on the summit, and as the fall of this man brought down those who were next to him, Manlius slew the others who clung to the rocks. The entire band was hurled down, and the Capitol was saved—by the sacred geese.

Famine, however, distressed both Rome and the Gauls, and a truce was made. And thus, while the Dictator Camillus was busily assembling an army, the defenders of the Capitol, worn out, having surmounted all human sufferings, and their arms weighing down their debilitated bodies, insisted that there should be either a surrender or that the Gauls should be bought off. The senate was convened. Instructions were given to the military tribunes to capitulate.

Brennus' terms were one thousand pounds weight of gold as the ransom of the Roman people. To this humiliating transaction insult was added. False weights were brought in by the Gauls, and when the Tribune Quintus Sulpicius objected, Brennus added his heavy sword to the weights on the scales, crying the insolent words: *"Vae Victis!*—Woe to the vanquished!"

The gods had decided otherwise—the Jupiter Capitolinus

who was soon to make the Romans rulers of the world. While the execrable ransom was being weighed against false weights, the Dictator Camillus came up and ordered the gold to be removed and the Gauls to leave. When they, holding out against him, affirmed that they had concluded a bargain, Camillus denied that the agreement was a valid one, having been entered into without his orders, and he gave notice to the Gauls to get ready to battle.

To his men Camillus said that their city was to be recovered with steel and not with gold. He pointed with his sword to the temples of the gods, to the sight of women and children and to the city disfigured by the calamities of war. He then drew up his army, as the nature of the place admitted, on the site of the half-demolished city, and the battle commenced. The gods assisted the Roman Eagles: the Gauls were routed with no greater difficulty than they had found in routing the Romans at Allia. Their camp was taken, and not one man was left to carry the news that Rome had defeated the Gauls. Camillus was acclaimed the Second Founder of the City.[1]

After the burning of the city by the Gauls, Rome had to struggle for her very existence. Before the city was rendered habitable again, it was announced that the Aequians and the Volscians were in arms. The Aequians had shared in the general disaster caused by the Gallic invasion, and their menace was therefore insignificant. But the Volscians boldly advanced to Lanuvium and once more encamped at the foot of the Alban Hills. Rome was in great alarm, and Camillus was once again named dictator. He defeated the Volscians and inflicted great losses, and pursued them into their own territory. He then marched rapidly to Bola, to which place the Aequians had advanced, and gained another victory.

But in the moment of triumph news came that Etruria was in arms. The Etruscans hoped by a brave effort to recover

---

[1] Livy, V.

the territory which the Romans had appropriated. They routed the Romans on the nones of July and captured Sutri; but Camillus by a prompt march recaptured it on the same day, and once again became the savior of Rome. He enjoyed a threefold triumph over the Volscians, the Aequians and the Etruscans.

Two years later, the Etruscan territory, now effectually conquered, was formed by the Romans into four tribes. By the addition of these new tribes, the first addition since this very territory was wrested from Rome by Porsenna, the population of Rome was raised to twenty-five tribes. The last Etruscan assault suggested to the Romans the wisdom of making the free inhabitants of this territory citizens of Rome. Here was the beginning of that sagacious policy whereby, for a time, political enfranchisement went hand in hand with conquest.

However, a few years after the temple of Concord was erected by old Camillus, fresh alarms arose. The Hernicans gave signs of disquietude and war had to be declared against them. Next year came the second invasion by the Gauls that showed again in the valley of the Anio, and had to be repulsed once more.

After this, Rome joined in league with the remaining Latin cities; the Gauls quitted Latium, and the few Latin cities which had rejected the alliance were compelled to yield. While these dangers were successfully averted on the northeastern frontier, the powerful Tarquinia declared war. The existence of the Roman-Latin League saved Rome. As it was, Rome found it hard to repel the Tarquinians, who made a sudden descent from the hills, defeated the Consul Caius Fabius and sacrificed three hundred and seven Roman prisoners to their gods. Two years later the Tarquinians, helped by the Faliscans, attacked again, bearing torches in their hands, their hair wreathed into snakelike tresses, driving the Romans before them and threatening the city itself. Eventually the Etruscans were beaten by a plebeian dictator, Marcius Rutilius, the first of his class to have advanced to this high office. The people of Caere joined the war, to assist the Tarquinians; they were defeated with the army of Tarquinia in a great battle. Three hundred and fifty-eight prisoners were scourged and beheaded in the forum in retaliation against Tarquinia.

Thus Rome carried through the dangers of surrounding wars and internecine strife, and rose stronger from every fall. She had now recovered all the Latin coast land from Mount Tibur to Circeii; and her increasing importance was shown by a renewed treaty with the great Carthage.

The sack of Rome by the Gauls also marked the dividing point between historical and ante-historical Rome, for the fire had wiped out not only the records but most of the monuments as well.

III

The fifth century was the most gratifying century for Rome. It was the century of the conquest of central Italy and the subjugation of all the peoples to the rule of Rome—the Latins, the Samnites, the Etruscans. Etruria during this epoch seemed to have cast into oblivion her very symbol, the bundle of fasces. Had she, even now, attacked Rome with her united power, she would have been more than a match for the proud republic; but the cord that bound the fasces, the bond of union which once united the lucumonies at the fanum of Voltumna, was now loose and broken. Piecemeal and one by one the lucumonies, no longer with formidable armies, and with faltering purpose, attacked Rome, and one by one they fell before Rome's unity and her gathering strength. In the same manner as they dissolved one into many, Rome gathered many into one, until she ruled alone and became the head of all Italian nations. Volsinia found the struggle unequal, because Faliscia had her hands fettered, and Clusium and Tarquinia could no longer be moved to her support.

After resting for some years, Rome turned to the south, against the Tarentines who had been the chief agents in exciting the Samnite war, and had now succeeded in inducing Etruscans, Umbrians and Gauls in the north, and Lucanians,

Bruttians and Samnites in the south to take arms simultaneously against Rome. The war with the Etruscans continued till the year 280, when, in consequence of the war with Pyrrhus the Tarentine, the Romans concluded a peace with them on easy terms. But the departure of Pyrrhus left all Italy at the mercy of Rome: the whole of the south to the very heel of the boot had now submitted to Rome; Brundusium became the Dover of Italy; the coast land between Umbria and the Marrucinians was occupied and their chief city, Asculum, taken by storm, and a portion of the people was transferred to the beautiful coast between Naples and the Silarus.

In Etruria, the ruling aristocracy had ventured to arm their serfs, but these men turned upon their masters. Volsinia called for help from Rome. Quintus Fabius, son of old Fabius Maximus, invested the city, and the Romans treated it as lawfully gotten booty. The ancient Etruscan town on the hilltop, with its polygonal walls, was destroyed; its two thousand statues and other works of art were transferred to Rome; a new town was founded on the low ground, which in the modernized name of Bolsena still preserves the memory of its ancient fame. After the fall of Volsinia all the Etruscan communities made formal submission. The shores of the sacred Lake Vadimon saw the last great battle between the Etruscans and the Romans, and in it the strength of the ancient nation was completely broken.

All Italy accepted the concession of a half-Roman citizenship—the appellation of *Socii et nomen Latini,* that was the technical expression for all the communities which were bound to supply soldiers to the Roman army. The Etruscan language was superseded officially by Latin. Truly, the fanum of Voltumna was in ruin.

The years went by—centuries! And yet the final vengeance of Rome upon Etruria was still to come. It was as though the hatred of Rome against the Etruscans, the insatiable hatred of the Roman plebs for the Tarquinians, went on and on, generation after generation, and might be appeased only by the destruction of the whole of Etruria and all the Etruscan people and their stupendous civilization.

We have now arrived at the date of the Second Punic War and the successes of Hannibal in Spain. The First Punic War lasted twenty-three years (264–241 B.C.), and was a most uninteresting war. The motive of it was to obtain the control of Sicily and expel the Carthaginians from the island, who, since the early times, had obtained possession of three factories or trading markets on the coast of Sicily—Panormus, Motya and Lilybaeum, which they fortified very strongly. When Pyrrhus undertook to expel the Carthaginians from Sicily, the appearance of the Carthaginian fleets off Ostia and in the Gulf of Tarentum roused the jealousy of the Roman Republic, and an opportunity only was needed to give rise to open war.

The contest was precipitated by the condition of things in Sicily, when it became clear that Syracuse and the other Greek cities of Sicily must now look for aid to Rome rather than to Greece; the acceptance of such an alliance on the part of Rome virtually implied war with Carthage. But all the great men of Rome, who had waged the Italian wars with so much vigor and ability, were now in their graves, and no worthy successors had arisen. The only men of note who appear on the Roman side during the First Punic War are Duilius and Regulus. Duilius, the admiral, appears for a brief time as the hero of the first part of the war; but in the second period the name of Marcus Attilius Regulus became famous, for his terrible death no less than for his patriotism.

After the naval battle of Ecnomus, the greatest battle that had ever been fought at sea, in which no fewer than three hundred thousand men were engaged, the Romans pursued the Carthaginians on African soil. The Roman consuls sailed straight across to the Hermaean Promontory which was not more than eighty miles from nearest point of Sicily, and, having landed their men, drew up the fleet on shore and fortified it as a naval camp. Then, marching southward, they took the city of Clupea by assault. No Carthaginian army met the Romans; every place they came near, except Utica, surrendered immediately, for they were unfortified and defenseless. Carthage, being mistress of the sea, feared no invaders and trusted to her ships for defense.

The consuls were advancing along the coast of the gulf toward Carthage, when Manlius was recalled to Rome with the greater part of the army, and Regulus was left in Africa with only fifteen thousand foot soldiers and five hundred cavalry. Yet he reached a point twenty miles from Carthage. The Carthaginians sued for peace: Regulus' terms were the surrender of the Carthaginian fleet, the cost of war and the cession of Sicily, with Sardinia, Corsica and the Balearic Isles. These terrible conditions aroused indignation, and the Carthaginians found a general in a soldier of fortune by the name of Xanthippus the Lacedaemonian. Xanthippus drew together all the mercenaries he could find, united them with the armed citizens, and supported by a large body of elephants he boldly took the field. He gained a surprisingly easy victory. Regulus himself was taken prisoner.

It was only two years later that the Romans recouped themselves at the battle of Panormus, when the Proconsul Caecilius Metellus defeated Hasdrubal, capturing thirteen Carthaginian generals and one hundred and twenty elephants, which were carried across the sea on strong rafts to celebrate the triumph of the proconsul. In commemoration of this victory the replica of an elephant was put on the coins.

After the battle of Panormus the hopes of the Romans rose again, and the senate gave orders to build a third fleet of two hundred ships. But the Carthaginians sued for peace. An emissary was sent to Rome to offer exchange of prisoners and to propose terms. Regulus was sent with this ambassador, under promise to return to Carthage if the purpose should fail. When he arrived at Rome he refused to enter the city as, being a prisoner, he considered himself no longer a citizen. The senate sent some of their members to confer with him in the presence of the Carthaginian ambassador, and Regulus told them: "Useless it is to ransom prisoners who surrender ignobly with Roman arms in their hands; let them be left to perish, and let the war continue until Carthage is subdued!" Peace was refused. And when Regulus returned to Carthage he suffered the vengeance of the Carthaginians. His eyelids were cut off; he was placed in a barrel lined with nails and rolled from the top of Carthage down to the walls, and then he was exposed to the glare of the African sun and left to die by the slow agonies of pain, thirst and fever.[1]

The interval between the end of the First Punic War and the beginning of the next was of nearly the same duration. In the course of this period (240–218 B.C.) both Rome and Carthage were involved in perilous wars. In the next three years Carthage was brought to the very brink of destruction by a mutiny of her mercenary troops, which had been employed in Sicily by Hamilcar and were now to be disbanded. Their leaders were Spendius, a runaway Campanian slave who feared to be given up to the Romans, and Matho, a Libyan who had been too forward in urging the demands of the army for their pay to hope for forgiveness by the Carthaginian government. Led on by these desperadoes, the soldiers gave full vent to their ferocity. They seized the Suffete Giscon who had been sent to treat with them; plundered the country; raised subject Africans in rebellion; besieged the fortified towns of Utica and Hippo, and cut off all communication by land with the promontory upon which Carthage so proudly rose. At the end of the second year, Hamilcar, who had in the meantime returned home, took command of the civic forces and forced Spendius to surrender: Matho was captured in Tunis and horribly sacrificed to the Goddess Tanit before the whole population of Carthage.

The forbearance shown by the Romans to Carthage during this fearful war between the mercenaries and Hamilcar, the enemy of Rome, makes their conduct the more surprising.

---

1 Polybius.

The mercenary troops in Sardinia had mutinied after the example of their brethren, and had taken possession of the island. After the close of the mercenaries' war in Africa, the Sardinian insurgents, fearing that their turn would come, put themselves under Roman protection. The Roman senate had the effrontery not only to demand the cession of Sardinia and Corsica but also the payment of a further sum of twelve hundred talents. The Carthaginians were too weak to refuse; but this ungenerous conduct made Hamilcar eager to take full vengeance on Rome. Hamilcar obtained independent authority above the narrow-minded Carthage's government, the Council of the Hundred. The leading members of the Council had long been jealous of the Barca family, of which Hamilcar was the chief; but now the Council agreed to his proposal to reduce Spain under Carthaginian power, especially as Carthage already had settlements in the south of the Iberian Peninsula. Hamilcar began thus to form the colossal army that he meant to bring overland against Rome.

But during this long period of peace with Carthage, encouraged by her success in Sicily and her newly acquired maritime power, Rome crossed the Adriatic against the Illyrians; and when the Epirotes sent ambassadors craving protection from Rome, the senate gladly took advantage of this opening, and sent a powerful fleet and army to Corcyra. The result was the opening of the road to win the good opinion of the Greeks, and indeed the Athenians and Corinthians received with high distinction the envoys who were sent to explain to the various Greek states the appearance of a Roman force in those quarters.

But while Rome was thus flirting with Greece a serious conflict was impending at home.

All the Etruscan maritime states, even those which no longer had any independent power, were rejoicing over the capture of Corsica and Sardinia by the Romans from the Carthaginians. The fact that these islands had been taken from them by the Carthaginians one hundred and fifty years previously still rankled and they had never forgiven the injury to their commerce. This was the main reason for the determined hostility shown by the Etruscans to the Carthaginian commander.

In the year 237 the Ligurian Gauls made war upon the Romans and continued it for six years. The Gauls now could become dangerous to Rome only by conquering and laying waste to Etruria, and in consequence they invaded and ravaged the rich state of Lucca. The Etruscans made a manful resistance, which prompted the Romans to consult the Sibylline Books. In the Libri Fatales it was found written that in cases of national peril they should bury alive in the forum two Gauls and two Greeks, one of each sex. This was accordingly done.

In the year 224 the Gauls from Venetia and Cenomania joined forces to drive back the Ligurians, and having disposed of them proceeded to make conquests among the Etruscan states. They came in formidable numbers, fifty thousand foot and twenty thousand horses, with many war chariots. The Etruscans called upon the Romans for help, and one consul came with twenty thousand men and reinforced his army with thirty-two thousand Etruscans, besides twenty thousand Umbrii.

The Gauls crossed the Apennines and marched by Lucca, Bologna and Clusium, bent upon a second sack of Rome. The Roman army was ambushed and defeated in Val di Chiana. Paulus Emilius made efforts to come to the rescue but arrived too late. The Gauls had withdrawn, laden with booty, resolved to carry their spoils home before attempting further conquests, and pursued their way along the course of the rivers.

The Consul Attilius, who had been engaged in Sardinia and knew nothing of what had happened in Italy, disembarked at this juncture at Pisa, and traveled along the Via Aurelia in his peaceful march to Rome. He was amazed to meet a large army of Gauls, all in battle array, at Telamon, whither they had been cautiously followed by Emilius. Attilius gave them battle, and the Gauls found themselves fighting two armies. They fled. Attilius was killed in the fight, but Emilius stood his ground, and the following year he completely subdued the Boii. The spirit of the Gauls seemed so humbled that the Romans anticipated their complete subjugation, which, however, was not realized till a long time afterward. The Romans had met more difficulties than they had anticipated by pursuing the Gauls, and it was two years before they were able to cross the Po and attack Mediolanum. The fall of this important city broke the spirit of the Gauls, who consented to a disadvantageous peace. Had the Etruscans entered into alliance with the Gauls, the fate of Italy would have been changed.

Hamilcar crossed the Straits of Gibraltar in 235 B.C. With him went his son-in-law Hasdrubal and his son Hannibal, then a boy nine years old, into whom his father was instilling those qualities which afterward made him the terror of Rome. Hamilcar had not intended to take his son to Spain, but the boy pleaded so earnestly that the father yielded, on condition that he should swear eternal enmity to Rome. Hannibal himself, in his old age, told this tale to Antiochus, King of Syria, and of how he was led to the altar of the gods of Carthage and took the direful oath.

Hamilcar fulfilled his promise to the Council of Carthage to conquer Spain and put Carthage in possession of a province which might become a great kingdom, worth many Sicilies and Sardinias. But the campaign of conquest and organization was a long one, and in the ninth year Hamilcar fell in battle. Seven years later Hasdrubal, his worthy successor, fell by the knife of an assassin.

Hannibal was in his twenty-eighth year when the Carthaginian army crossed the Alps—nearly the same age as Napoleon Bonaparte when he led the army of the French Republic by the same route into Italy. While he was on the south of the Ebro, laying siege to the ancient Greek colony of Saguntum, the Roman senate had sent envoys to Hannibal requiring him to desist from attacking a colony belonging to their ally, Greece. Hannibal replied coldly that he could not answer for the ambassadors' safety in his camp; they had better seek redress at Carthage. When the news of the fall of Saguntum reached Rome, the senate sent an embassy to Carthage to demand that Hannibal should be given up. The enemies of the Barca family would probably have complied; but Rome was hated in Carthage, and the Council replied that Saguntum was not mentioned in the treaty of Hamilcar. One of the Roman envoys, Quintus Fabius, doubled his toga in his hand, held it up and said: "In this fold I carry peace and war: choose which you will have." The Suffete replied: "Give us which you will." "Then take war," said the Roman, letting his toga fall loose. "We accept the gift," cried the Council of Carthage, "and welcome it!"

Hannibal possessed every quality of a great commander. His physical strength and activity were such that he could handle his men's arms better than they could, whether on foot or on horseback; and his endurance of heat and cold, of fatigue and hunger, excelled that of the hardiest soldier in the camp. He never required others to do what he could not and would not do himself. To these bodily powers he added qualities of ability and military knowledge fully as great as those of his father, Hamilcar. His frank manners and genial temper endeared him to the troops while his strong will made them follow him to a man.

Despite the hardships which his mixed army of Africans and Spaniards, Gauls and Italians underwent for sixteen years in a foreign land, there was never a single mutiny in his camp. His quick perception and great sagacity enabled him to make accurate forecasts of future events, and he formed his plans only after careful investigation and inquiry.

He was also said to have been cruel to the point of ferocity and treacherous beyond measure, but there is no record of a single occasion on which Hannibal broke faith with Rome. He was indifferent to human life; but he was also capable of noble magnanimity toward a worthy enemy—he was indeed a great general. To penetrate with an army from the

Ebro to the Po across giant mountain ranges barring his progress, without accurate knowledge of the route, was a mighty undertaking, and to have accomplished this march with triumphant success would alone justify the homage which is paid to the genius of Hannibal.

Many ancient historians have written of Hannibal's passage over the Alps, with incredible tales of that voyage. The only credible thing is that Hannibal conducted it like a wise and able captain. He found that he had to meet two enemies: the local populations and the obstacles of nature. His men he kept in spirit and fortitude by inspiring them—as Napoleon inspired his army so many centuries later—describing to them the country which they would find spread at the foot of those mountains they were now to pass, and that Nature had designed as a rampart to cover and defend the very land awaiting them on the other side. If the native Allobroges passed those mountains as part of their ordinary life, Hannibal's army could pass them as well.

The descent, however, proved harder than the ascent. The army came to a place where neither their elephants nor horses could march. Fresh snow appeared at first to give footing firm enough to the soldiers, but soon this became slush, and under it was the frozen snow of the previous year, which made it impossible to march, none being able to keep their feet. Many were lost in crevasses or over precipices.

Hannibal encamped his army at the entrance to this pass, and ordered the snow to be removed from the ground. By excruciating pains and labor he at length made a passage through it. In the meantime he ordered the Numidians to make a passage for the elephants, which took three days of labor among all sorts of difficulties; but at last a way was made also for the elephants, which had suffered a great deal.

It took Hannibal fifteen days to cross the Alps, and it cost his army the loss of many men and beasts, but five months after his departure from New Carthage he could boldly advance into the northern plain of Italy, lying about the River Po. Of the troops that had marched out with him there now remained twelve thousand Africans, eight thousand Spaniards and six thousand cavalry. This information is according to his own accounts, engraved on the column at Lacinium.[1]

The war which began with the invasion of Italy lasted seventeen years. It can be divided into four periods. The first is the victorious career of Hannibal from the passage of the Alps to Capua, marked by famous battles—Trebia, Lake Trasimene, Cannae. In the second period the Romans recover Capua but lose Tarentum. In the third, Hannibal, left without support from Carthage, is confined in the mountains of Calabria, and it ends with the disastrous battle of the Metaurus. The fourth and conclusive period, in which Hannibal stands at bay at the extreme tip of southern Italy, ends with the great battle of Zama, of which Polybius has left a vivid description.

The Etruscans saw Hannibal suddenly appear upon the plains of Liguria, inviting the Gauls to join him, promising them freedom and spoils, victory and revenge. The Gauls joined him, and the Ligurians, who had most recently suffered from Roman hauteur, insisted upon marching through the Etruscan territories, now subjected to Rome. Hannibal offered the Etruscans their complete independence and also agreed to restore their ancient policy; but the ancient Etruscan spirit was now broken—they were busily engaged in active commerce, and there was much jealousy and competition between the surviving cities. Besides, the Carthaginians had for ages been the Etruscans' rivals and enemies in commerce and naval warfare. The Etruscan contingents joined the Consul Flaminius at Arretium—and in the circumstances, they could do no other. Haruspices were now sent from Etruria to explain portents in the Latin state, to which the native augurs were unequal. An inglorious end for a great nation!

When Scipio followed Hannibal across the sea, the Etruscans responded with alacrity to the appeal for a fleet. Perugia, Clusium and Rusella cut down fir trees to provide the ships

---

1 Polybius.

with masts; Caere victualed the fleet; Populonia contributed iron from her foundries, Volterra tackling and corn, Tarquinia sail from her factories, and Arretium contributed, besides grain, thirty thousand helmets, thirty thousand spears, axes, swords, javelins, pikes and halberds, along with water vessels and machines for forty ships of war. Etruria had become a wealthy and useful kind of dominion from which Rome could draw supplies for her imperial wars! After the battle of Zama and the conclusion of the Second Punic War, the Romans, in order to liquidate their vast expenses, ventured to tax their colonies and allies. The states that objected to these measures were instantly deprived of the *Jus Italicum*. Etruria was not mulcted, for generous contributions made her secure.

IV

Now also the Third Punic War had been waged and won—Carthage was no more. Scipio "the African" had razed it to the ground. Six days and six nights without respite lasted the slaughter of the Carthaginians inside their city, with the soldiers relieved from time to time by fresh ones, lest the continual killing and horror should make their hearts fail. People died a thousand different sorts of deaths, some at the sword's point, some were thrown headlong down from the tops of the houses to the pavements below, while others were run through with javelins, pikes and swords.

When Scipio gained the foot of the fortress all the streets were in flame. The fire devoured everything—the conical roofs of the heptagonal temples, the steps that rose to the higher districts of the wealthy, the terraces, the streets of the lower districts crowded with shops, the vast granaries, the immense docks, the splendid gardens. On the sixth day what had been a splendid city was a mass of ruins shrouded in dense smoke. The hill of the Acropolis with its magnificent monuments had disappeared, the temples with their twisted columns and capitals of gilded bronze, the cupolas of copper, the vast metopes of Numidian marble, the obelisks standing on their tips like reversed torches, the marvelous buildings,

the beautiful colonnades, the majestic walls of granite—
everything was in ruins.

Scipio watched the fighting and the slaughter for six days
and six nights without sleeping. He was continually in action,
taking his food in snatches, and fought until he was ex-
hausted. Then, worn out, he sat down in a prominent place
so that he might still observe the conquest. On the seventh
day the surviving Carthaginians came to him bringing in
their hands the vervain of Aesculapius, and begged for clem-
ency. Hasdrubal came privately with a branch of olive in his
hand, and Scipio commanded him to prostrate himself at his
feet. Then he let the soldiers plunder the city.

The historian Polybius, who had been his tutor, says that
when Scipio stood contemplating the city which had flourished for seven hundred years, famous for its arms, for its
fleet, for its elephants, for its riches and wealth, and renowned also for generosity and resolution—seeing it now absolutely ruined, he wept. The same tragedy had befallen
Troy, and from his lips came the couplet of Homer:

> *Priam's and Troy's time come, they Fates obey,*
> *And must to fire and sword be made a prey.*[1]

When all the booty was collected, Scipio amassed all the
bucklers, arms, war engines and useless ships, and having
girded himself in the manner of the Romans, with his own
hand he set fire to them as a sacrifice to Mars and Minerva.

But Rome, when the senate and the citizens heard the
great news that Carthage was conquered and destroyed, sent
orders to Scipio to raze to the ground every single house that
remained in Carthage so that only ashes should be seen of
what had been Carthage, and no one should ever attempt to
rebuild it, no one should ever inhabit the place again. Like-
wise they ordered that all the cities which in the war had
taken the enemy's part should also be razed. Rome was merciless.

---

[1] Appianus.

Now the power of Rome knew no limits, nor did her ambitions. The history of Rome in the last century and a half B.C. reads like a terrifying list of wars in which the Romans were always victorious—the Macedonian War, the Achaean War, the Spanish War, the Jugurthine War, the Cimbrian War that took the Romans into Germany. Everywhere Rome was conquering. Rome had now conquered a vast empire; Rome ruled the world.

She evolved, she created a *Jus Italicum* which she applied to all the conquered nations and peoples; but it was not a *Jus Gentium,* the rights of man; it was the law of the conqueror over the conquered. While morality, good faith and self-denial prevailed among themselves, these values were not observed in their dealings with other nations. It was, one must admit, the great defect of all antiquity. The calmest of Greek philosophers, Aristotle, regarded as barbarians the slaves of the Greeks. International law in the modern sense was unknown except in the formalities of declaring war and making peace and in the respect paid to the persons of ambassadors.

The spirits of the victors were elated to the highest pitch. The Etruscans dared to falter in their allegiance to Rome; but the Lex Julia ordered all citizens of the subjugated states of Italy to come in person to Rome and demand the freedom of the city within sixty days—and the concession was, after all, more specious than real! Nevertheless, it served to impart new hopes to the Italians, to distract their councils, and to relax and break the sinews of resistance.

Then, Rome saw the beginning of civil war: the rivalry of her two most fortunate generals became the main channel of the history of Rome. In the year which closed the contest of the republic with her dependent allies—88 B.C.—Sulla was forty-nine years old, Marius about seventy. Sulla was enjoying the warm breeze of popularity and renown, while Marius, wearied but not sated with honors, was moodily throwing away the advantages. From campaign to campaign Sulla had dogged the steps of the old warrior, always ready to step in and seize the opportunities which the other cast recklessly in his way.

Marius' jealousy was prompted by the contrast between their respective births and origins. Marius was of humble Volscian origin; Sulla, though needy to the point of poverty, was a scion of the illustrious house of the Cornelii, and preened himself on the distinction and advantage such a lineage conferred. Sulla was trained in the accomplishments of Hellenic learning; Marius, conscious of his lack of them, vainly affected to despise education.

Sulla wrote and spoke Greek; his memoirs of his own life became the textbook of the Greek historians of Rome. But this veneer of superior culture seems to have failed to cover the rough plebeian nature that was the core of Sulla's character. For Sulla was one of many noble Romans who combined pretensions to culture with the love of gross debauchery and pleasure in the society of mimes and vulgar jesters. He was a coarse sensualist, and by his disregard of the nuptial ties he offended even the lax morals of his times.

His eyes were of a piercing and pale blue, and his sinister expression was heightened by the coarseness of his complexion, which was disfigured by pimples and blotches. The raillery of the Greeks compared his skin to a mulberry sprinkled with meal. With age, this condition turned into a repulsive disease, and his whole body became covered with festering sores which seemed to breed lice. Sulla's manners were haughty and morose; nor is there any act of kindliness or generosity recorded of him. The nobles who accepted him as their champion had no personal liking for him. He despised the isolated ascendancy of Marius, and meant to rule in Rome at the head of an oligarchy.

The Civil War was based on the eternal conflict in Rome between the patricians and the plebeians, the aristocracy and the people. But there was another point, and it was a highly political one. Marius was a new man; he was a man from a conquered and subjected land; a man upon whom the Roman senate had reluctantly conferred full Roman citizenship because of his military successes. Marius in his heart entirely approved of the claims of the Socii—the conquered allies. "Where was the supremacy of Rome," Sulla asked, "if all the Socii were to be granted full citizenship? They were more numerous than the Romans. They would swamp the Romans in their own elections held in their cities." Marius, on the other hand, required the votes of the plebs, and as he knew that all the new citizens would be with him, he was resolved to obtain full Roman citizenship for them.

Sulla won, and his victory was marked by the proscriptions. The corpse of the great Marius himself, which had been buried and not burned, was torn from its sepulcher on the banks of the Anio and cast into the stream. This desecration was an impiety of which Rome had hitherto furnished no example. The troubled ghost, said the poet of the Civil War, continued to haunt the spot on the eve of calamities.

The proscriptions and victims were so numerous that Catulus asked Sulla in the senate: "Whom then shall we keep to enjoy our victory with, if blood continues to flow in our cities as abundantly as on the battlefield?" Sulla coldly replied that he had not yet decided whom he would spare.

One young man, however, was spared—a kinsman of Marius, whose aunt, Julia, had been the wife of Marius. He was a young man of eighteen. The vestals interceded for him, and some of Sulla's own adherents raised their voices in his favor, pleading his youth. Sulla spared him: "I spare him, but beware! In that young trifler there is more than one Marius." The young man's name was Caius Julius Caesar.

And now, with the rule of Sulla, came the end of Etruria. The Etruscans had taken the part of Marius, and when Marius had returned from Africa and had landed at Telamon, five thousand Etruscan volunteers joined his standards and marched with him from Ostia to his last occupation of Rome. Upon his death the Etruscans were still faithful to Marius' cause, which was the cause of freedom for the subjected people.

Sulla took it upon himself to punish the Etruscans—to complete in the most relentless way the vengeance of Lucius Brutus upon the last of the Tarquinians. Sulla took all the beautiful cities of the Etruscans. He dismantled them, destroyed their public buildings, burned their records, toppled their monuments, razed their walls. Instead of Fiesole upon its towering height, he built Florentia in the plains and made it a military colony. Arretium suffered least because Cicero was its patron. Volterra resisted the Sullan army for two full years, and was not taken till 83 B.C., the year of Sulla's death. But in that same year Volterra's loyal daughter Populonia was all but destroyed.

Sulla's principle of government was to exterminate all his opponents. He deprived every Etruscan city of the right to exist by denying its share in the public lands. Sulla fined, taxed and turned into colonies the whole of Etruria, and distributed the land to his forty-seven legions. The booty was so immense, in gold, in silver, in goods of all kinds, in works of art, in Eastern carpets, in richly dressed slaves, that Etruria was left bare—all that was left of the ancient and wealthy Etruscan cities were their cemeteries. And one wonders what superstitious fear held back Sulla's hand.

So completely destroyed was Etruria, such a thing of the past did it become that Varro, writing in the last century B.C., talked of the Etruscan language and civilization in terms of archaeology; and Cicero followed suit with his *De Antiquitate*.

Only the indestructible survived—the Etruscans' culture, their art, the spirit of their civilization, that continued to supply Rome with sculptures and all artistic work, while the doctors and dentists opened schools of medicine in Rome and became personal physicians to the wealthy and powerful. But above all, the Etruscan religion survived, for it was the religion of Rome, and the Etruscan haruspices found a field in the city for their divinations, albeit Cicero coined the quip, "When a diviner meets another diviner, he can't suppress a smile."

The Etruscan language was now dead; no one in Rome could understand it any longer; it was now a pastime for scholars and erudite persons, or for the young men of the upper classes who followed a course in the ancient disciplina as a special title in their exams for the civil service, or as an apprenticeship in the religious rituals of political offices.

According to the ancient tradition the power of the Etruscan nation was to last 1,100 years beginning with the year 434 before the founding of Rome,[1] and ending about the year 665 of Rome, or 87 B.C. The Etruscans therefore looked upon their fate as inevitable. Had not the haruspices heard the shrill blast of a trumpet in the skies and a voice proclaiming in tones of loudest brass that the age of the Etruscan dominion was at an end?

But the spirit of Etruria lived on in Rome, in spite of democratic venom and aristocratic contempt for the "obese Etruscans." And so it happened that when the empire was a reality and nothing more could change Rome's destiny, and the laureate poet Virgil invented a full-dressed Latin origin for Rome, Augustus, first emperor and proclaimer of the Augustan Age, ordered that the Sibylline Books should be taken into the temple of his personal protector Apollo, and there be preserved forever as sacred texts to be consulted in the hours of need—the books that the Sibyl had sold, so many centuries ago, to King Tarquin the Etruscan.

---

[1] 1187 B.C.

BIBLIOGRAPHY

ANCIENT SOURCES

APPIANUS: *Romana Historia.*
AULUS GELLIUS: *Noctes Atticae.*
CICERO: *De Divinatione, De Natura Deorum.*
DIODORUS SICULUS: *Bibliotheca Historica.*
DIONYSIUS OF HALICARNASSUS: *Roman Antiquities.*
HERODOTUS: *Historiae.*
LIVY: *Ab Urbe Condita.*
PLINY THE ELDER: *Naturalis Historia.*
PLUTARCH: *Vitae.*
STRABO: *Geography.*
TACITUS: *Annales.*
VARRO: *De Lingua Latina.*

MODERN WORKS

BLOCH R.: *The Etruscans.*
BUONAMICI G.: *Fonti di Storia Etrusca.*
CARTER: *Religious Life of Ancient Rome.*
CLES-REDEN S.: *Das Versunkene Volk.*
DENNIS G.: *The Cities and Cemeteries of Etruria.*
DUCATI P.: *Etruria Antica, Le Problème Etrusque.*
FELL R.: *Etruria and Rome.*
GIGLIOLI G.: *L'Arte Etrusca.*
HUS A.: *Les Etrusques Peuple Secret.*
MARTHA: *L'Art Etrusque.*
MOMMSEN T.: *Römische Geschichte.*
MULLER K.: *Die Etrusker.*
NIEBUHR B. G.: *Römische Geschichte.*
NOGARA B.: *Gli Etruschi e la loro Civiltà.*
PALLOTTINO M.: *Gli Etruschi.*
PFISTER K.: *Die Etrusker.*
RIVERS G.: *The Heroines: Lucretia, Wife of Collatinus.*
SOLARI A.: *La Vita Pubblica e Privata degli Etruschi.*

INDEX